AÇAI

D1044116

An Extraordinary Antioxidant-Rich Palm Fruit from the Amazon.

Second Edition

Alexander G. Schauss, PhD, FACN

Biosocial Publications
Tacoma, WA

Açai: An Extraordinary Antioxidant-Rich Palm Fruit from the Amazon.
Second Edition.

© 2009 BioSocial Publications

October 2009

Manufactured in the United States

ISBN 978-0-9814906-4-9

Library of Congress Cataloging-in-Publication Data

Schauss, Alexander 1948 –

BioSocial Publications

P.O. Box 1174

Tacoma, WA 98401

www.biosocialpublications.com

Disclaimer:

This work on the Açai berry is not intended to be an exhaustive or scholarly
technical work. Given the increasing interest in the Açai berry, the intention of
this book is to provide the public with some useful information on the subject.

The reader should not interpret any of the information in this book as medical
advice. If you believe you have any symptoms, condition or disease, always
consult a licensed health care practitioner or physician.

Table of Contents

Preface

Introduction

Preface

Numerous studies on açai have been published which help us gain an understanding of the palm fruit's properties in terms of human health.

Comparisons between "superfruits" and uncertainty as to what fruit to consume disregards advice that we should be eating more fruits and vegetables, rather than relying on any one or two to get the antioxidants we need. These comparisons have led to deceptive studies and arbitrary criteria that try to prove one fruit is better than another, claiming that appearance, availability, for example, is as important as demonstrated evidence of the food's bioactivity. There really is no need for such competition in terms of human nutrition as a variety of colorful fruits and berries should be a part of our diet in order to get the widest range of phytochemicals from plant foods. That's what our nomadic ancestors did and it is good advice today.

Unscrupulous companies have used dubious endorsements to encourage consumers to buy certain foods. Many of these companies are engaged in flagrant and unlawful consumer fraud practices. They advertise on the internet that taking supplements of one product or another will result in rapid weight loss, yet no studies exist to substantiate such claims. Reputable companies whose açai-based juice products are sold around the world are funding numerous independent safety and efficacy studies to learn more about açai and its properties.

Of further interest is the continued growth in demand for açai fruit. This demand is having a favorable affect, not only in terms of its positive impact on the Amazon economically but because it's slowing down the destruction of the Amazon. As Brazil increasingly recognizes the value of these palm trees, the thought of allowing more clear cutting of biologically diverse land for cattle or planting soya becomes more difficult to justify. Around the world we have paid a steep ecological and social price by relying on industrial methods for food production, a system that is based on mechanization, biotechnology, pesticides and fertilizers, and monoculture. The end result has fed us during the 20th century, but at what price? To deplete and contaminate or soil and water resources? To lose a biodiversity that might take thousands of years to regain?

As demand for açai fruit and other foods available in the Amazon grows we may finally see an end to the destruction of the rain forest that only years ago seemed unstoppable.

As more is learned about açai I begin to wonder if the açai palm tree isn't a tree of life. It is sustainable, requires no chemicals to grow, is disease resistant, and provides a nutrient-rich fruit found to process potent anti-inflammatory properties of benefit to human health. Found abundantly growing within the largest rain forest in the world, this formerly obscure palm trees' fronds not only provide a canopy that traps moisture and protects the ecology beneath it from equatorial radiation but may yield for us an a greater understanding of the mechanisms that affect aging and our health. Given the tons of carbon the Amazon absorbs and the oxygen it produces and releases each day, the interest in and contribution açai plays in protecting the "lungs of the Earth" could not have come soon enough.

Alexander G. Schauss, PhD, FACN

Introduction

Fruit and vegetable consumption is associated with a marked reduction in heart and vascular diseases. These foods contain many vitamins, minerals, trace elements, and phytochemicals, which may change the composition of the flora in our intestines and increase the amount of roughage and fiber that passes through us. This can slow down carbohydrate metabolism, thereby modulating the rapid increase in blood sugar after meals, reducing a key risk factor associated with cardiovascular disease. Fruits and vegetables are also low in calories and can replace processed foods that provide little more than calories. Eat a couple of apples, and you are less likely to have room for that chocolate cake or bag of chips!

But which fruit or vegetable is best for you? How often should you eat them? There are so many to choose from, and their cost can vary dramatically in price and availability.

This book is about a fruit that grows on a palm tree in the Amazon, known by its Latin name as *Euterpe oleracea*, and by natives living in the Brazilian Amazon as "açai" (ah-sigh-ee).

The first chapter shares information about this author's life that led him to take an interest in açai. You will read about some fascinating people I was fortunate enough to meet over the years.

Chapter two provides information about palms, how they develop and deal with the environmental stresses of the rain forest in order to survive. What are free radicals and antioxidants? What is oxidative stress and how do free radicals and antioxidants affect our health and play a role in aging and disease?

In the third chapter, more information on the açai palm and its habitat in the Amazon is provided. A helpful illustration of the taxonomy of a palm tree is offered to help visualize how the fruit grows and is harvested. A discussion is provided on the effect harvesting palm trees for their heart-of-palm has on the Amazon and how altering agricultural practices is restoring a fragile ecosystem.

Chapter four is about the açai fruit, including its historical use as a food as reported by British, Portuguese and American botanists over the last two hundred and fifty years, along with a list of synonyms used to refer to açai in the southern hemisphere.

The rise in popularity of açai as a food is covered in chapter five, particularly in the United States, which today is the biggest importer of açai fruit in the world.

The food uses of açai are discussed in chapter six. How does it reach markets outside of the Amazon, especially given how perishable it is?

In chapter seven, the macro and micro nutrient composition of açai is discussed, including that of vitamins, minerals, amino acids, and fatty acids, as well as other components. What evidence is there that açai may possess health benefits in terms of cardiovascular health, inflammatory diseases, degenerative diseases, and overall protection from oxidative stress?

Chapter eight discusses antioxidants in more depth. The role of flavonoids in food and the phytochemicals identified in açai are presented. The role of polyphenols, proanthocyanins and anthocyanins, is covered, particularly those compounds at the center of attention in berry and fruit research. Açai is particularly rich in anthocyanins such as cyanidin-3-rutinoside, which has been found to selectively kill cancer cells *in vitro*, while leaving healthy cells alone. What emerging evidence is there that this may occur in the body too?

In chapter nine, attention is drawn to how the antioxidant capacity of a food is determined, using ORAC, TEAC, FRAP, NORAC, HORAC, and SORAC assays. How free radical quenching and assay scores relate to a food and whether it has bioactivity or not?

Chapter ten continues the discussion of antioxidants, more specifically in terms of the antioxidant capacity of açai.

The second to last chapter discusses the benefits of antioxidants. Since açai has been shown to have exceptional antioxidant capacity, how might this play a role in reducing stress, inflammation, and inhibition of lipid peroxidation?

The last chapter provides a numerical summary of key points made in the book, ending with concluding remarks that define the importance of this palm fruit in terms of its growing popularity.

Chapter 1

Gathering the Tools for Discovery

It is indeed strange how key events in one's life can be interconnected.

While working toward a degree in history and sociology at the University of New Mexico (UNM) in Albuquerque in the late 1960's, I decided to explore a region of southern New Mexico called the Mimbres Valley on weekends. I learned that at one time a tribe of Indians had settled this valley and then disappeared. No one knew what happened.

Due to a combination of research and luck, I discovered pottery and other artifacts of this long lost tribe, which I brought back to the history department for further study. As a result this findings significance I was invited to join and inducted into *Phi Alpha Theta*, the national honorary society in history, during my sophomore year.

While searching for evidence of the Mimbres' previous existence within a 25 square mile area, a most unusual occurrence led to my discovery. I spotted a butterfly that seemed out of place in the middle of the desert. I ran after it for nearly a quarter of a mile. It directed me to a spring. There, lying by a small pool of water were several pieces of pottery protruding through the sand. Some shards had paintings that resembled animal figures. After leaving markers to show where each shard was found, I took a few pieces back to the university to be examined, and the rest is history.

It turned out that the Mimbres Indians left the valley after more than 25 miles of the river near their settlement had run dry following prolonged drought. Possibly they moved south, or headed west for the Mogollon Mountains (which are now a part of the Gila National Forest), or maybe the tribe resettled north, somewhere along the Rio Grande River. To this day, no one knows exactly where the Mimbres Indians might have resettled, or if they just simply perished.

The following summer, after completing my junior year at UNM, I took a sociology course at the City University of New York (CUNY) in upper Manhattan. An opportunity arose that allowed me to study a theory involving the effect of very high doses of ascorbic acid (vitamin C) on opioid receptors in the treatment of withdrawal symptoms in heroin addicts. An opioid is a chemical substance that has a morphine-like action in the body.

To test my theory, I was allowed to work with a group of heroin addicts, just a few blocks from CUNY's campus, not far from Columbia University. My research project led to the development of a protocol that was used by street addicts to withdraw from their addiction within a two-week period – without the usual withdrawal symptoms.

The study demonstrated that if addicts hooked on heroin took enough ascorbic acid dissolved in water or juice each day in divided doses, they could withdraw from their addiction without experiencing any significant side effects. Going through complete withdrawal, known as "going cold turkey," was the only other option available at that time. The experience was both brutal and painful. It discouraged addicts from seeking treatment, or only when they reached such a high daily dose of heroin that they could no longer support their habit.

We discovered an interesting "side effect" during the study. Those addicts, who had a viral infection known as hepatitis A when they started treatment, were no longer infected with the virus after they completed the protocol. Apparently the high doses of vitamin C killed the virus that caused hepatitis A (or assisted the immune system to overcome this viral infection).

A second discovery occurred quite by chance, when these addicts returned to the street after successfully freeing themselves from their addiction to heroin by following the vitamin C regime. The addicts discovered (to their dismay, I am sure) that if they tried to get high on heroin again they could not experience the same euphoria, due to the blocking effect vitamin C had on opioid receptors.

This situation occurred because the high dose of vitamin C occupied certain opioid receptor sites in the brain. These sites blocked the heroin from creating the altered state (the "high") addicts sought. The success of this treatment in the field of addiction research led to my being contacted by many physicians and public health officials.

These studies in New York City proved to be my first exposure to antioxidants. It certainly made me wonder what other attributes these compounds had.

Ten years later a team of investigators with the National Institute on Drug Abuse at the National Institutes of Health (NIH) came to Seattle, Washington, to evaluate the effectiveness of this treatment regime during my tenure as Director of the Institute for Biosocial Research at City University in Seattle.

King County's addiction treatment services director, Dr. Janice Keller-Phelps, M.D., showed them how she had been using it with hard-core addicts. A noted expert on addictions with years of experience working with addicts in Maryland and Washington, D.C., before coming to Washington State, she comparaed the results to a cure for cancer. After four days interviewing addicts NIDA's team left impressed.

Unfortunately, apparent pressure to promote a new drug under development at the time called methadone kept NIDA's findings quiet, something I continue to shake my head about even after 30 years.

Hence, the effectiveness of oral vitamin C therapy for the treatment of heroin addiction remains largely unknown. In recent years, numerous addiction scientists are beginning to acknowledge the shortcoming of this drug, but that has not done much to revive interest in vitamin C as an option.

The results of this vitamin C research attracted the attention of Dr. Linus Pauling, the two-time Nobel laureate, who had taken an interest in the therapeutic benefits of this vitamin at the time. In 1978 I decided to write about the research in New York and sent a manuscript to a publisher in Berkeley, California who happened to know Dr. Pauling. To my surprise, when the book came out Dr. Pauling's signature appearing on the cover along a quote from him.

A few years later, in 1983, I was invited by the McCarrison Society in England to give a series of lectures about research on nutrition and behavior. The invited lectures were presented during the European Conference on Nutrition and Behavior, held at Oxford University. Among some 200 attendees, who hailed from a number of highly regarded European institutions, was the newly elected President of the Society, Professor Hugh McDonald Sinclair. Knighted by Queen Elizabeth, Sinclair had studied animal physiology at Oriel College, Oxford. Later, he taught biochemistry at Oxford, where he was a Senior Demy at Oxford's medical school, Magdalen College. Dr. Sinclair completed his studies in medicine at the University College Hospital Medical School in London, where he subsequently became a lecturer in physiology at University College, London.

Most British people who lived in England during World War II know Dr. Sinclair as Winston Churchill's advisor on nutrition as the Minister of Food for the UK. A few years after the World War II, Dr. Sinclair was awarded the U.S. Presidential Medal of Freedom, and became an honorary Brigadier General of the British Army for his contributions to the war effort.

Born in 1910, Professor Sinclair became one of the 20th century's outstanding experts in human nutrition. He became widely known for claiming that "diseases of civilization," such as coronary heart disease, cancer, diabetes, inflammation, stroke and skin disease, were all made worse by "bad fats."

Today we know that hydrogenated oils are indeed a leading dietary contributor to coronary heart disease and stroke, but that fact wasn't apparent back in the 1940's and 1950's. Dr. Sinclair pleaded with the dietetic community and food companies to only use healthy fats, such as the monounsaturated fatty acids found in olive oil, avocado oil, nuts, and fish oils. Sinclair realized that the food industry had shifted its priorities from that of providing foods of quality to producing foods based on profit, shelf life and taste. Michael Pollan mirrors this opinion in his book, *In Defense of Food*:

"A diet based on quantity rather than quality has ushered a new creature onto the world stage: the human being who manages to be both overfed and undernourished, two characteristics seldom found in the same body in the long natural history of our species."

After the publication of my lectures in a British nutrition journal, subsequently reviewed in the *Sunday London Times*, Dr. Sinclair invited me to return to Oxford. He wanted me to teach a course with Professor Joseph Egger, MD, pediatric immunologist, to be presented at the John Radcliff Hospital at Oxford, on the effect of food on behavior. Dr. Egger held joint professorships at the University of London and the University of Munich, and was well known for his research on food allergies in children, a topic we shared a strong interest in.

Moving to Oxford gave me the opportunity to spend hours in the university's remarkable libraries, and to periodically visit Professor Sinclair at his extraordinary home in Sutton Courtenay (just outside of Oxford). He had a remarkable library that contained numerous collections left to him including those of many Nobel Laureates.

The opportunity of living in Oxford resulted in my decision to increase my attentions in the study of ethnobotany and the role of botanicals in human health. Professor Sinclair shared with me the field research he conducted in the Arctic, where he had lived on a diet identical to the native Inuit's. This furthered my awareness of how much could be learned from observing what native populations consumed. Documenting in remarkable detail the effects on his health from living on an Inuit diet led to the recognition of the importance of long-chain fatty acids, found in fish, and their effect on inhibiting blood platelets from aggregating (clotting) and thus reduce the incidence of thrombosis (blood clots) that contribute to heart attacks and strokes.

Having access to Oxford University's amazing Radcliffe Library made living in Oxford an experience I will always cherish.

During one meeting with Professor Sinclair, I mentioned an experience that I had undergone several years earlier, during a visit to Australia to lecture that was held at the University of New South Wales School of Law. I had just arrived in Sydney, after completing the first phase of field research in Guam. I was trying to determine both the cause of Guamanian Parkinson's disease, an atypical form of Parkinson's disease, as well as the unusually short lifespan of men who lived on the island. Some of my suspicions that the prevalence of Parkinson's disease might be linked to a fruit growing on the island were not greeted with much support. Today we know that indeed it is linked to the disease and contains a potent neurotoxic agent that has been shown experimentally to induce the same symptoms as seen in patients diagnosed with this form of Parkinson's disease. But then we don't think that a fruit could be harmful. This lesson taught me that although we might believe in a food's safety, there is no substitute for experimental evidence and a full understanding of its chemical composition to confirm our beliefs. Foods produce chemicals to protect themselves, some of these compounds are toxic, whether acutely so or if consumed chronically over time.

Unfortunately, just about the time I left Guam to fly to Australia, I caught a cold. By noon of the following day, not many hours after I had arrived in Sydney, my temperature had risen to nearly 105 degrees Fahrenheit. I was getting extremely weak and of course worried that my lecture that evening would be cancelled. Given my condition, Dr. Archie Kalokerinos, M.D., was called to the house by my host. How grateful I am today to have met a most remarkable physician whom I might never have known.

Dr. Kalokerinos, the recipient of the Australian Medal of Merit just two years earlier in 1978, had begun using vitamin C to treat Aboriginal infants. He made a connection between their vitamin C status and how they responded to receiving childhood vaccinations. Prior to his discovery of the importance of vitamin C in infants and young children, one in every two Aboriginal children died within a week after receiving a series of vaccinations intended to boost their resistance to certain infectious diseases brought to Australia by settlers. He discovered that a single one-gram shot of vitamin C, administered as an injection into the child's muscles, just a week before vaccinations were given, would prevent such deaths. Dr. Kalokineros' book, *Every Second Child*, is a fascinating account of this lifesaving discovery and the impact it had on stirring up a national controversy. A movie was made about his work some years later based on his 1981 book.

Upon his arrival at my sickbed, Dr. Kalokineros immediately began administering an intravenous (IV) drip of ascorbic acid (pure vitamin C) into my body. Over the course of hours, my temperature lowered so that by 6 pm my temperature had dropped to a comfortable 99 degrees, along with a surprising surge of energy. That evening I started my lecture as originally scheduled at 7:30 pm, and lectured straight through to 10 pm. I still recall how my mind seemed incredibly able to recall facts and citations without difficulty.

His autobiography, *Medical Pioneer of the 20th Century*, is fascinating reading. The last time I had contact with the good doctor, he had been appointed an Honorary Medical Advisor for Aboriginal Health.

Professor Sinclair and Dr. Kalokineros both advocated the restriction of excessive amounts of refined carbohydrates, particularly sugar. This approach did not particularly win over Sinclair or Kalokineros with the World Sugar Council in London or the Sugar Council in Washington D.C., or any of its allies. These were empty calories, Sinclair argued, that provided little more than calories.

Dr. Sinclair predicted that the world would suffer from an epidemic of obesity, due to the consumption of foods low in nutritional density. He referred to this health care crisis as "over-consumption malnutrition." He passed away in 1990, but his theories and warnings are gaining acceptance and recognition around the world. For example, in August 2009, the American Heart Association sent our a press release that urged people to reduce their sugar intake from an average of 22 teaspoons a day to less than half that amount because "experts think eating too much sugar" is one of the reason that two-thirds of Americans are overweight or obese. Why did it take so long for the AHA to declare their support for a reduction in sugar consumption? It was an empty source of calories one hundred years ago, and still is today. Moderate and occasional use of sugar should have been what was taught all along.

These seemingly unrelated experiences in New Mexico, New York City, Oxford, Seattle, and Sydney, helped me to recognize the existence and importance of seeking out foods that could contribute to our health while avoiding those foods that were toxic to our health.

I think of these mentors and many others I have been fortunate to learn so much from as being akin to that butterfly which led me to discover traces of the lost tribe of Mimbres Indians. Without their guidance and knowledge, I might never have realized the importance of studying a relatively unknown and obscure palm fruit growing in the flood plains and rain forest of the Amazon.

Chapter 2
What is "Açai"?

On one of my trips to Europe, I had the fortune of stopping in the town of Coimbra in central Portugal. This historical city is the home of the University of Coimbra, the second oldest university in the world. Founded in 1290 by King Dinis, the University sits on a hill above Avenida Emidio Navarro, which runs parallel to the Mondego River (Rio Mondego). Hiking up the narrow cobblestone streets to the University's central square is an experience in itself.

I desired to do some research in the library of the University's Anthropology Museum and Laboratory (known as the Faculty of Sciences and Technology). One of the department's faculty members invited me to view its remarkable and priceless display of ancient Amazonian Indian masks. These treasures are kept in a secured area of the museum, not open to the public.

Among the many masks on display were those of the now extinct Jurupixuna Indians, who had lived in the Orinoco basin of Brazil. The Jurupixunas perished, shortly after making contact with European explorers who found their settlements in the late 18th century.

Unfortunately, with the arrival of European explorers and settlers to the Western hemisphere, there also came many diseases such as smallpox, for which the native population possessed no immunity. As these diseases spread from village to village, thousands of Indians died; their immune systems were unable to repel the contagious pathogens.

Early accounts by Portuguese Europeans exploring the region detailed the use of masks worn during dances. These rituals honored the birth of a child, a marriage, recognized a successful hunting expedition, or celebrated the completion of the season's harvest of a palm fruit. I thought, "A palm fruit?" Yes, a palm fruit. Why did they have a dance specifically to honor the harvesting of a palm fruit?

This information, recorded by explorer's centuries ago, supported the concept that the Amazon basin grew foods with unusual properties. This palm fruit must have had extraordinary attributes, possibly unlike any other food in the world.

It was only in the late 20th century that scientists realized that foods not only possess nutrients and calories, but also contain phytochemicals equally as important as vitamins and minerals in contributing to our health. Some natural chemicals found in plants are able to prevent, mitigate or treat many different diseases or afflictions.

We now recognize that our forests, plains, coastlines and jungles all hold a literal pharmacy of compounds that are produced by tens of thousands of terrestrial plant species, marine plants and microorganisms.

Among more than 2,000 species of palms presently growing around the world, only a few types provide fruit that humans can consume. Coconuts and dates are two well-known examples of palm fruits. But neither coconuts nor dates are found growing in the Amazon, and neither is known for its antioxidant capacity.

Certainly, there could be foods that experience oxidative stress in other regions of the world, and therefore have high antioxidant activity to protect the plant. Plants have developed special physiologic defense compounds. Some of these compounds can be found more concentrated in plants that grow near the equator.

Plants derive their energy from the sun. Billions of years ago, powerful solar rays bombarded the Earth. These rays were so harmful to life that simple cells had to figure out a way of surviving without being roasted. As the Earth's rotation slowed down, its magnetic field deflected much of the sun's most toxic radiation. This set the stage for Earth to use the sun's radiation to facilitate life forms. In time, plants flourished, but they still had to cope with the amount of radiation that could reach the earth's surface.

To survive the damaging effects of ultraviolet (UV) radiation in particular, plants needed not only to have the ability to use the sun's energy, but ways to effectively eliminate oxidative damage to their cells. This requirement is the reason terrestrial plants learned how to combine chemicals and form compounds such as polyphenols, a class of flavonoids with protective antioxidant activity.

Flavonoid pigments, which reflect ultraviolet light, were one early evolutionary response to the dangers of direct sunlight. Other compounds such as anthocyanins, which will be discussed in some depth, also reflect mutation-causing ultraviolet light.

Plants can't run away when threatened by UV radiation. They need to have a chemical means of defending themselves. Grasses, which started to proliferate on our Earth about 80 million years ago, have had far more time than humans to figure out how to protect themselves from oxidative stress. We have developed limited ways of protecting ourselves from reactive oxygen species, called free radicals, induced by our environment, which can be harmful to our health.

What are Free Radicals?

Dr. John Janowiak has spent years figuring out how best to explain to nutrition students what a free radical is. Let me share his explanation and modify it slightly to make it as easy to understand as possible.

In order to understand how free radicals affect body organs and systems it is best to begin with a simplified model of the atom.

The nucleus, a core region of an atom, consists of a number of protons and neutrons. Electrons spend as much time as possible near the nucleus and as far away from each other by moving in different orbitals, which are regions of space around the nucleus in which electrons are likely to be at any instant. Each orbital has enough room for two electrons at most.

Free radicals are atoms or groups of atoms that can cause damage to our cells, impairing our immune system and leading to infections and various degenerative diseases.

Free radicals have lost one of the electrons that keep them chemically stable and in their frenetic search for a replacement, they'll steal one from another molecule, which in turn will steal another molecule's electron, etc., until the cycle is stopped by the body's antioxidants.

Until stopped, free radicals damage DNA, proteins, lipids (implicated in heart disease), carbohydrates, and body tissues (lining of the arteries, the eyes, etc.) causing cell and tissue degeneration.

Some of the diseases to which free radicals are thought to contribute are cancer, atherosclerosis, stroke, myocardial infarction, senile cataracts, Parkinson's disease, autoimmune diseases, osteoarthritis, and the aging process.

Free radicals are simply the waste products of ordinary metabolic processes, such as breathing and immune reactions. Thus, some oxidant activity eludes control and is beneficial to the body.

But environmental free radicals are destructive; such as ionizing radiation, air pollutants, toxic industrial chemicals, pesticides, cigarette smoke, and some drugs. Other sources of free radicals come from over doing exercise, over-heating cooking oils (deep-fat frying), consuming hydrogenated oils, overexposure to the sun's rays, and chronic stress.

Humans do manufacture some "endogenous antioxidants." These are compounds that our bodies make to counter the damaging effects to our cells caused by free radicals. When demands on our cells are not extraordinary, our cells do a marvelous job of helping us deal with these free radicals.

When a critical imbalance happens between the productions of reactive oxygen species (ROS), reactive nitrogen species (RNS), and antioxidant defense systems, animal cells are at a definite disadvantage. That inability to provide a complete defense is the reason why we want to supplement our diet with antioxidant-rich foods.

The fruit of a palm tree with a history of traditional use as a food seemed a viable candidate. Especially a very tall palm tree – so tall, that it actually formed the canopy of the Amazon rain forest. Just think of the amount of UV exposure that such a tree must be able to cope with every single day growing at the equator. But with so many palms…which one?

In addition, if it was growing in the tropics, this palm tree might also have to withstand the effect of flooding, a common problem. With each flood, its roots would be shut off from the oxygen it needs. Palms in rain forests have adapted to flooding by special spiny root structures called pneumatophores. Without them these palms could not survive when rivers and tributaries overflow.

The most promising rain forest to explore was in Brazil. There I learned about a palm called, "açai." Could this palm contain a "mother lode" of antioxidants found in a food, given the relentless oxidative stress that it experiences?

I learned that botanists know the açai palm by its Latin name, *Euterpe oleracea.* Natives pronounce it, "Ah-sigh-ee."

Studies of the açai berry, performed in Brazil prior to our research, mentioned that this fruit contained compounds called polyphenols – but then, so do most colorful fruits.

However, beyond initial analyses on some of the nutrient content (vitamins and minerals) of the fruit, our literature search discovered that no one had conducted a systematic study of its chemistry, identified its predominant and minor flavonoid compounds, or examined its other chemical and biological properties. We contacted scientists in Brazil. Their generously provided offerings were meager, reflecting how little was still known about this palm fruit, despite its abundance. Most of the information dealt with how it impacted the state or county economically, or contained information of far more interest to anthropologists and ecologists. Knowledge of its composition was limited, particularly its phytochemical make-up and bioactivity.

In the formative stages of my studies, I made the discovery that the açai fruit had extraordinary antioxidant capacity *in vitro* (out of the body) compared to any fruit or vegetable I was familiar with. Keeping that a secret for several years was not easy as I had to contact laboratories, food scientists, and chemists, many of whom were also looking for novel foods with demonstrated antioxidant activity. It was best not to bias other scientists who would obtain samples of the fruit from me, to see if they confirmed my finding. Whenever I needed to perform another study, I didn't mark the sample as being freeze-dried açai pulp. I wanted their objective opinions based on the results.

I also determined that the freeze-dried form of the pulp and skin of the fruit retained the highest level of antioxidants able to scavenge free radicals *in vitro*, compared to any other food preservation method.

Freeze-drying produced a well-preserved product to study; certainly superior to spray-dried açai, which most processors in Brazil offered. We also tried out other methods of food preservation of açai fruit, including refractance window drying, thin film drying, and sun drying. Refractance drying had potential, but there wasn't equipment available anywhere in the southern hemisphere.

It has been known by food scientists for decades that there are two ways to preserve nearly 100% of the nutritional benefits of a fruit or vegetable, namely, freeze-drying or flash freezing. Freeze-drying is done in a vacuum, limiting the activation of enzymes, which would otherwise quickly break down compounds in the fruit that contribute to its antioxidant capacity. However, freeze-drying was ten times more expensive than spray drying.

A lot has been learned about the effect of processing on fruit and berry flavonoids, particularly the antioxidant polyphenols. Spray drying is done with heat. Major losses of monomeric polyphenolic anthocyanins occur during storage of thermally processed fruit and berries. Since these anthocyanin compounds contribute to açai's antioxidant activity, it made no sense to use spray-dried material for research.

Using a reliable and validated method for determining the oxygen radical absorbance capacity (ORAC) of a food against the peroxyl radical *in vitro*, I researched what kinds of antioxidant capacity the pulp had, if any.

We were surprised to see that açai pulp did have considerable antioxidant activity. Over time, we would discover that açai had the ability to quench the peroxynitrite radical, hydroxyl radical, superoxide radical, and peroxyl radical, based on various assays.

Some free radicals are the product of the interaction of two free radicals. For example, a potent oxidant among nitrogen-derived free radicals is peroxynitrite, which is formed by the interaction of superoxide and nitric oxide. It is considered to be more powerful than its precursors because of its powerful oxidation action, which can cause damage to lipids, proteins, and DNA. We looked at the ability of açai pulp to scavenge peroxynitrite and the assay showed it did.

Oxidative Stress

Oxidative stress is increased production of reactive oxygen species (ROS), in amounts that exceed cellular antioxidant defenses.

A supplier of reagents used by scientists (a division of OXIS research) has come up with one of the best explanations of what oxidative stress is, and why it is important for everyone to understand. Through this, we appreciate the reason we need to reduce oxidative stress by making sound lifestyle changes and insuring that we consume ample antioxidants from food.

"Oxidative stress occurs when the generation of reactive oxygen species (ROS) in a system exceeds the system's ability to neutralize and eliminate them. The imbalance can result from a lack of antioxidant capacity caused by a disturbance in production, distribution, or by an overabundance of ROS from an environmental or behavioral stressor. If not regulated properly, the excess ROS can damage a cell's lipids, protein or DNA, inhibiting normal function. Because of this, oxidative stress has been implicated in a growing list of human diseases as well as in the aging process."

The Discovery of the Importance of Antioxidants

How was the importance of antioxidants in dealing with the damaging effects of oxidative stress discovered? By now you understand that antioxidants work by stabilizing free radicals thereby limiting the damage they might otherwise cause. But it wasn't always so obvious.

Dr. James Joseph, PhD, a noted neuroscientist who has been doing research on antioxidants for several decades, works at the Jean Meyer USDA Human Nutrition Research Center on Aging located at Tufts University in Boston. In his book, *The Color Code*, he recalls that during the initial development of the ORAC assay in the early 1990's, a popular magazine dispensed with scientific terminology and simply called ORAC units "anti-aging points." At first he was reluctant to accept this description, but it didn't take him long to reconsider.

He went on to explain that this concept is not a bad way to think of ORAC scores, because the evidence is clear that people with sufficient amounts of antioxidants in their diet show the fewest effects of aging. How he reached this conclusion is worth retelling.

The brain primarily uses glucose for fuel. This preference explains why carbohydrates are broken down to their simplest unit – a glucose molecule – so the brain can use it for energy. In fact, the brain uses more glucose, by far, than any other organ or tissue in the human body.

However, the process of churning and metabolizing glucose, mainly to produce energy for the brain to function well, also produces free radicals – lots of free radicals. Normally, the body can counteract these free radicals, but in some situations the body cannot accomplish this balance. When that happens, the brain experiences oxidative stress, and can literally age prematurely.

To illustrate this phenomenon, a study was conducted at the University of Colorado Health Sciences Center in Denver. It was this study that changed Dr. Joseph's understanding of the importance of antioxidants.

At the Center, the effect of toxic amounts of oxygen on aging was illustrated in an experiment using rats. The animals were placed in an oxygen chamber, and for 48 hours they were exposed to 100% pure oxygen. After just two days, the research group discovered that the average level of brain activity of the rats had declined to such a degree that their brains had literally aged from 6 months of age to 18 months. The researchers based this estimation on the rats' performance on various brain tests. In human terms, this change is equivalent to watching our brains age from 18 years old to 60 years old.

When the rats were placed back on the same kind of air that we normally breathe, containing approximately 21% oxygen, the damage experienced gradually reversed. This demonstrated that the body's antioxidant system could gradually counter the effects of oxidative stress. This beneficial change occurs mainly by eliminating the source of oxidative stress, and also by allowing the brain to use the antioxidants that are produced in the body and obtained from one's diet.

Then the research group asked a profound question. Could a diet rich in antioxidants, given prior to such an experiment, protect the brain of these rats in this same 100% oxygen environment? So back into the oxygen chamber went those poor rats. But this time, they had been fed a diet rich in foods having high ORAC scores, such as blueberries, for several weeks.

To the experimenters' complete surprise, after two days of breathing 100% pure oxygen, the rats on the ORAC-rich diet experienced NO measurable deterioration; the brains looked and performed normally! So, referring to ORAC scores of foods as "anti-aging points" is not very much off the mark.

Another way of understanding free radicals is to think of rusty metal. Rust is caused by oxygen. The faster you rust, the faster you age. So when you think of free radicals, think of ways to slow down their effects; in other words, consider rusting more slowly.

You can see the effect of oxygen when you bite into an apple. Before long, the area where you bite turns brown, due to an enzyme called polyphenol oxidase. If you apply an anti-oxidant (such as a solution of vitamin C), to the bite, it stays white, and doesn't turn brown. The color does not change, because now the apple doesn't need to release enzymes, since the vitamin C is doing the work as an antioxidant.

Vitamin C prevents the enzymatic reaction that turns the apple's pulp brown after exposure to oxygen. Hence, an exogenous antioxidant (one that comes from the diet) can reduce the demand for an endogenous antioxidant (one made in the body or, in this case, the apple), to protect it from the damaging effect of oxygen associated with reactive oxygen species.

Our diet provides wonderful exogenous antioxidants. That simple fact is the reason why researchers world-wide have been looking for foods rich in antioxidants, ever since we discovered a way to measure their antioxidant scavenging capacity.

Oxidative stress caused by free radicals has been identified as a major factor in the progression of aging, and also contributes to numerous diseases. Therefore, the ideal "anti-oxidants" act like a sponge, mopping up or removing excessive oxygen radicals before they can harm healthy cells, but without interfering with the benefits that free radicals provide.

Free radicals can actually help the immune system rid the body of invading pathogens, cells that have lost their ability to function, and cancer cells. The goal is to strike the proper balance between the actions of oxidants and antioxidants.

One would think there is a consensus among scientists that antioxidants foods will prevent or treat age-related diseases. However, not all researchers agree with this premise. Part of the reason for this controversy is the difficulty of gathering evidence from long-term intervention studies. Although all kinds of claims have been made that the stilbene, resveratrol, found in red wine, is a magic anti-aging compound, studies to prove this have been disappointing when the results are applied to aging in humans. Studies by Zou and colleagues published in *Experimental Gerontology* in 2009 found that resveratrol had no meaningful effect on life extension when studied in flies.

Consider that in many parts of the world, prior to the introduction of agriculture, humans consumed at least 800 different kinds of plant foods annually. This knowledge comes from the study of fecal remains (coprology) left by our ancestors suggesting that they lived for thousands of years eating a highly diverse, plant-based diet, with few exceptions. Compare the variety of plant foods they ate with the limited number of plant foods available to us today in our supermarkets.

Recent studies on populations living around the world suggest that a diet rich in fruits and vegetables might contribute to a lower incidence of many diseases.

In Michael Pollan's book, *The Omnivore's Dilemma*, he wrote:

"The koala [bear] doesn't worry about what to eat: If it looks and smells like a eucalyptus leaf, it must be dinner. The koala's culinary preferences are hardwired in its genes. But for omnivores like us a vast amount of brain space and time must be devoted to figuring out which of all the many potential dishes nature lays on us to eat."

Many anthropologists believe that the reason we evolved such big and intricate brains was precisely to help us deal with the omnivore's dilemma. Unlike other animals, we humans have the distinct advantage of the accumulated wisdom learned from eons of diet to make sound choices. How are we doing? Rather poorly. Just look about us. If you live in the United States, two-thirds of Americans are overweight or obese. Let's use our brains and make sound choices that don't place us at risk of all kinds of illnesses and age-related degenerative diseases.

Chapter 3
The Açai Palm Tree and the Amazon

Açai grows in a palm tree native to the Amazon. The fruit from the palm, *Euterpe oleracea*, requires humid soil conditions to grow. A diversity of plants (such as aningas, aturias, murues, murumurus, buritis, and jarandubas) grows along the edge of the rivers and shelters the more inland-growing açai palm. Two related native palm species, other than *E. oleracea*, also grow in the Amazon and are known to botanists by their Latin names as *Euterpe edulis* and *Euterpe precatoria*. Sometimes the fruit from these palm trees is also referred to as açai. However, the more common name for the fruit of *Euterpe edulis* is either "juçara" or "juçara."

In Brazil, where both palm trees grow, juçara is not consumed as often as açai due to a shorter harvest season, although both have similar appearances when ripe.

The botanical nomenclature or origin of the species *Euterpe oleracea* can best be understood by seeing its biological position and relationship:

Kingdom	*Plantae* – plants
Subkingdom	*Tracheobionta* – vascular plants
Superdivision	*Spermatophyta* – seed plants
Division	*Magnoliophyta* – flowering plants
Class	*Liliopsida* - monocotyledons (monocots)
Subclass	*Arecidae*
Order	*Arecales*
Family	*Arecaceae* – palm family
Genus	*Euterpe* – palm
Species	*Euterpe oleracea* Martius – the açai palm

Occasionally you will see the açai palm described by its Latin name ending with either the word "Mart.", or the name, "Martius." Karl Friedrich Philipp von Martius was a famous German botanist who lived in the early 19th century and is best known for his work on Brazilian flora, including the 15-volume work, *Flora Brasiliensis*. He was the first to publish a description of the palm, hence is given credit by inclusion of his last name after the Latin name for açai.

Palms belong within the plant family known as Arecaceae, which consists of nearly 4,000 species that grow primarily in the tropics and subtropics. Within the palm family are over 200 genera (the plural for genus). Nearly 220 different palm species have been identified in the Amazon.

The origin of the word, *Euterpe*, comes from the Greek for "forest grace," owing to its elegant appearance. Its dropping leaflets give the long pendulous fronds the appearance that rain has just fallen on them. Botanists and gardeners consider members of the genus *Euterpe* to be some of the most attractive ornamental palms found in nature. *Euterpe* palms have been described as graceful and easily recognizable, owing to their slender, gray stems, prominent crown shaft, and narrow, pendulous leaflets.

Euterpe was also a Greek goddess of song and poetry, one of the nine muses of Greek mythology.

Brazilians love to consume açai mixed with other fruits before a late evening of socializing, dancing or playing sports. They report it gives them increased energy and a sense of wellbeing. Açai has none of the addictive or diuretic qualities associated with beverages such as coffee or tea that contain stimulants, such as caffeine, so it is easy to understand their preference for the fruit pulp.

Euterpe oleracea is a palm species unique to the New World. Only 40 species of *Euterpe* exist in the world. Three species of this genus provide edible fruit: (i) *E. precatoria*, (ii) *E. edulis*, and (iii) *E. oleracea*, all found within the Amazon. Two lesser-known palms are found in the Amazon, one occurring in Guyana, *Euterpe longibracteata*, and another found primarily in the northern region of the Andes in Peru and Ecuador, *Euterpe catinga* var. *roraimae*.

Interestingly, the açai fruit is far from being the only palm fruit that humans consume. The coconut palm (*Cocos nucifera*) gives us coconuts. In the ancient Sanskrit language of India, the coconut is called *kelpa vriksha*, meaning "the tree that provides all the necessities of life." Another familiar palm is the date palm (*Phoenix dactylifera*), which is extensively cultivated for its edible fruit. The date fruit can be eaten soft, or hard, or dehydrated, or ground and mixed with grain to form a nutritious feedstock for dogs, horses, and camels. Hence, the idea of eating a palm fruit isn't strange or unusual. Nevertheless, not all palm fruits are edible; in fact, the vast majority of palm fruits are inedible, unless you are a bird or insect. Yet palms have other characteristics that distinguish them.

Palms are monocots. They are very different from dicots, which are trees such as elms, maples, oaks, walnuts, pines, firs, and all fruit-bearing trees, familiar to those of us who live in more temperate climates. The difference between monocots and dicots is important in understanding the ecological and nutritional issues related to açai fruit.

If you cut off the top of a tree that is a dicot, the tree does not die. Instead it sends out new branches, one or more of which will try to replace the missing limb. By contrast, if you cut off the top most palm trees, no lateral branches or limbs will form, and most will die within a few weeks to months. Dicots tend to send roots deep into the earth, especially via a main taproot. But palm trees are capable of only lateral root growth. They spread roots out in every direction from the trunk, just below ground level. The roots of some palms have been measured and found to extend for well in a radius over 100 feet [30 meters] from the parent trunk.

Another distinction between the two types of trees is the fact that dicots have root hairs designed to absorb nutrients and water, while palm roots do not have such hairs. Because palm roots grow just under ground level, they are close to the extensive areas of decomposing organic materials that filter nutrients directly to the root system. In the Amazon, an enormous amount of organic matter falls on the ground, nourishing palm trees.

Palms also have several other ways of obtaining nutrients, which are different from the nutrition gathering methods of dicots. One of the most important distinctions is the fact that palms have what are known as vascular bundles. These bundles contain a highly developed network of cells that transfer carbohydrates manufactured in the leaves to other parts of the plant. Other bundles act as a conduit, to conduct the water and dissolved minerals that have been absorbed by the roots.

A palm fruit consists of three layers: a thin outer surface called the epicarp; a thick, fleshy, middle fibrous section called the mesocarp (pulp); and another thick innermost layer called the endocarp. If you have ever eaten a husked coconut purchased in a supermarket, you were eating a palm fruit that has been cleaned down to the endocarp level (its thick innermost layer).

Many dicots are grown via a technique called tissue culturing. Tissue culturing consists of taking a piece of a plant (such as a stem tip, node, meristem, embryo, or even a seed) and placing it in a sterile, usually gel-based, nutrient medium where it proliferates. Palms, however, are very difficult to grow using this method. Attempts to grow the açai palm from tissue cultures have been unsuccessful to date. Even if it is achieved, there are many other variables involved in ensuring the success of the palm's growth and development, all of which affects the quality of its fruit.

The only palm species that have been successfully tissue cultured are two commercially important species: *Elaeis guineensis*, from which palm oil is derived, and *Phoenix dactylifera*, the date palm that produces dates.

The only source of açai fruit comes from palm trees growing wild, or cultivated on plantations in the equatorial regions of the Amazon where the açai palm grows naturally. The palms require an average of 90 inches

(2,300 mm) of rain a year. Simply put, it likes water. The açai palm is a native of the floodplains of the eastern Amazon River basin, where it occurs in some regions as large, nearly monospecific stands. The stands are actually clumps of palms that might be several feet from each other. Each clump may have from several to as many as 24 trees.

In the most eastern section of the basin, near the Atlantic Ocean, açai palms grow in nearly pure stands on elevated islands in the flood plains. These islands are subjected to annual flooding. As many as 9,720 palm trunks (growing among some 2,000 clumps) have been recorded per hectare (2.47 acres) according to a study reported by Calzavara in 1972 and cited in a 1986 study of foods found in the Amazon commissioned by the Food and Agriculture Organization (FAO) of the United Nations. On drier soils the density is less, in the range of 4,000 to 7,000 trees (800 to 1,400 clumps) per hectare. A more recent survey conducted by the Brazilian government found that in many areas of the eastern basin up to 7,500 açai palms grow per hectare. Consider that just 625 açai palms per hectare can produce 15 tons of fruit, and you get a sense of how much fruit is available for harvesting the three million hectares of the Amazon covered with açai palms!

Figure 1 shows the typical taxonomy of a palm tree.

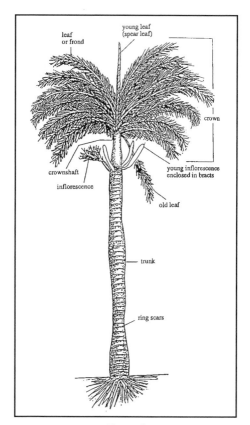

Figure 1

In looking at Figure 1, you will note that just below the crown-shaft and fronds is a cluster of branches called the "inflorescence." The fruit of the palm develops on rachillas that bear cream-colored flowers borne in 3's, a central female and 2 lateral males, bearing 80-130 rachillae. Flowering and fruiting occurs throughout the year, usually producing from four to eight inflorescences each year per adult tree. When the fruit is ripe it can yield up to 200 fruit ~0.6 inches (~1.5 cm) in diameter per branch.

Once ripe, those trained to climb these majestic trees will cut off the downward hanging branches holding as much as 200 fruit. Thousands of families are involved in gathering and bringing the fruit to central storage facilities via canoes and motorboats to brokers or markets where they are sold in baskets, each weighing on average 26-28 pounds (11.8-12.7 kilos). An açai palm can produce over 2,200 lbs (1,000 kilos) of fruit during its productive years.

As demand for the fruit increases, the economic value of the fruit increases as well. This has resulted in an extraordinary shift in attitudes among many Brazilians, as well as the Brazilian government. As more açai is exported, bringing to Brazil foreign currency, the need to protect these majestic palms has become apparent. Starting in 2007, there is growing evidence that preserving forests of these palms is in the best economic interest of the Amazon and the entire country.

To contribute to saving what is left of the Amazon, Norway made an extraordinary donation of one billion dollars to the Brazilian government to reduce deforestation. The agreement was signed in September 2008 during Norwegian Prime Minister Jens Stoltenberg's visit with Brazilian President Luiz Inacio Lula da Silva. The agreement to provide funds through 2015 includes a cooperative agreement on research and development. Funds will be tied to radar surveillance of Brazil to see if the country is reducing deforestation and forest deterioration.

This paradigm shift in foreign support comes at a crucial time. There is considerable debate worldwide about global warming. The cause is attributed to the dramatic increase in the use of carbon-based fossil fuels, particularly oil and natural gas. However, it may also be due to natural shifts in climate. Regardless of which theory is right, the impact of global warming is already being felt.

It is worth noting that the Amazon rain forest produces an estimated 20% of the oxygen on this planet. Something to think about, as 21% of the air we breathe is oxygen.

In 2005 and 2006, the Amazon saw the worst drought in decades; each year it could get worse. Conditions in the Amazon have become so bad that thousands of square kilometers burn at a time, polluting the air, closing airports, and causing children and the elderly to be hospitalized for respiratory problems. I've seen the same scenario many times during visits to Indonesia where man-made fires may be as large as five million acres on the island of Sumatra alone. During one visit to Padang, Sumatra, the pollution index rose to 875, so bad that you could not see the hood on your car, much less find a way out of the city either by car or plane. Any attempt to drive more than a few miles per hour was suicidal or homicidal depending on who ran into you or whom you hit. Children and the elderly died of respiratory failure. The same is happening on Borneo Island, Indonesia, and other tropical countries who do little to control such fires. With each fire, more carbon goes into the air. Who knows what plant medicines are lost forever. Malaysia put a stop to such forest fires years ago, so stopping the practice is possible.

More than 100 million metric tons of carbon were released in the Amazon in 2005 and 2006 due to fires. While less than 20 percent of the Amazon rainforest has been destroyed, every effort needs to be made to stop any further destruction. Otherwise, it is estimated that by 2050, more than 40 percent of the Amazon rainforest will be wiped out, and with it an incredible storehouse of wildlife and plants. Figure 2., shows just how extensive the Amazon is. The white line is the demarcation of the Amazon.

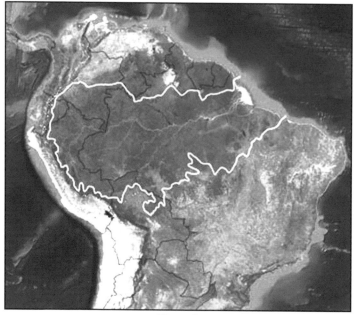

Figure 2

The disintegration of the Amazon ecosystem, with the release of massive amounts of carbon, could be a significant factor in pushing us into a runaway greenhouse problem.

The tropical area known as the Amazon is the range and habitat for açai and juçara palm trees found at elevations from sea level to nearly 3,300 feet (1,000 meters). In recent years, botanists have identified açai palms near the border of Brazil and Colombia, more than 2,500 miles west from the mouth of the Amazon River and the Atlantic Ocean.

In the northwest part of the Amazon, the Wanano Indians refer to açai fruit as "*wipi*." The tribe rates açai as a "first-ranked" fruit – very important to their hierarchical social system, which involves the exchange of important foods. This ranking has been reported for many other tribes, suggesting that açai fruit has been an important part of the diet of humans in the Amazon for thousands of years as reported in 2009 in a chapter on açai in a book on bioactive fruits and vegetables edited by Watson and Preedy.

The Heart-of-Palm

The palm, *E. edulis*, commonly called *juçara*, is the major source of palm hearts produced in Brazil. Vast groves of juçara palms have disappeared due to over-harvesting. Brazilians prefer the palm hearts that come from juçara.

When you add "heart-of-palm" as a garnish to a salad, you're eating the young leaf crown shaft of the tree, known as the "spear." Refer to Figure 2 to see where the palm hearts are obtained and then recall the difference between a monocot and a dicot tree. A palm's spear grows only at the top of the tree. This spear may only be a few feet in length. To obtain this section from certain palm trees, the entire palm will die; hence, a palm tree 20 to 40 feet (6 to 12 meters) will disappear from the forest.

I am not against eating palm hearts, but not at the expense of rain forest lands that need protection from encroachment by humans. Primates, birds and insects, etc., need these palms as a source of shade, food and shelter.

The Wall Street Journal released a report on this problem that appeared on its front page with the heading, *"In Brazil, a Desperate Struggle is Waged Over a Salad Garnish."* In the article, the *Journal* reported that poachers were illegally chopping down 5,000 to 10,000 palm trees each week, just to obtain 12-to-16 inches (30 cm to 40 cm) of the palm tree's crown/shaft.

According to Brazilian law enforcement authorities, a poacher engaged in this activity can cut down an average of 50 trees every day to earn roughly $1 a tree. Once chopped down, the heart-of-palm is extracted. In one area of Brazil, the decimation has been so severe that only 7% of the original Atlantic forest remains standing. With fewer palms available, poachers are now beginning to encroach into other areas of Brazil, including the famous Itatiaia National Park (*Parque Nacional do Itatiaia*), southwest of Rio de Janeiro, known for its waterfalls and 250 species of birds.

Armed guards are trying to move poachers out of national parks, but unfortunately, there are few national parks encompassing concentrations of açai palms. There is only one national park, for example, in Para state: the Amazonia National Park (*Parque Nacional de Amazônia*), north of the Rio Tapajós. It covers an area of 2,250,000 acres (1,000,000 hectares). Unfortunately, gold prospectors have recently destroyed at least 10% of the park. The palm-hackers are now taking their illegal activity further north into the Amazon, where large stands and groves of wild *E. oleracea* grow.

What makes this distressing situation even more poignant is the fact that heart-of-palm, itself, has no particular nutritional value as a vegetable beyond its fiber content.

Alternative Sources of Heart-of-Palm

Recent worldwide interest in açai fruit is having a profound effect on many people living in the Amazon. Residents are beginning to realize that cutting down palm trees for the heart-of-palm is not in their long-term interest, unless trees need to be culled and the heart-of-palm removed from old trees too risky to climb or reduce the number of trees in a clump to increase fruit yield.

Due to the dynamics of supply and demand, countries in South and Central America have created plantations solely for the purpose of producing heart-of-palm. Ecuador and Guatemala have become leading producers of heart-of-palm. Instead of cutting down juçara or açai palm trees, they grow the peach palm tree (*Bactris gasipaes*), also known as "Pejibaye", to obtain heart-of-palm for markets around the world.

People relying on açai for income remain ever vigilant against poachers. Older palms are a highly sought after target for heart-of-palm poachers because such palms can yield up to 50 pounds of palm hearts per tree.

Even though Ecuador and Guatemala have become major exporters of heart-of-palm, the açai palm, which only grows in the Amazon, has become a major source of the Brazilian heart-of- palm industry. As Brazil encourages the development of plantations using peach palms rather than either açai or juçara palms, fewer of these trees will be targets.

Fortunately for açai, several characteristics limit its potential as a significant source of heart-of-palm. The most important of these is the presence of polyphenoloxidase and peroxidase enzymes that discolor the palm heart upon contact with air. Consumers prefer the whitest palm hearts. By comparison, the peach palm lacks these enzymes while also being slightly sweet.

Fortunately, açai palms can regenerate from seed. Over time areas that were over-harvested can be restored; however, it takes decades to replace. The açai palm is a part of a larger ecosystem, during which time much of the ecology will have changed, including the prospect that other species native to the area of destruction may become extinct. In some cases, no matter how much regeneration occurs, the destruction may be too late to return the forest back to its original state. This reality has begun to happen.

From May 2000 to August 2005, Brazil lost more than 51,000 square miles (nearly 132,000 sq. km) of forest, an area the size of Louisiana, or the country of Nicaragua. In 2004 and 2005, the deforestation of the Amazon rain forest was the second worst ever observed, according to the Brazilian government. Satellite photos taken between 2003 and 2004 show that ranchers, soybean farmers, and loggers, burned and/or cut down a near record 10,088 square miles (26,128 sq. kilometers) of rain forest. Between 2005 and 2006, the Amazon lost another 6,450 square miles (16,700 sq. km), an area greater than the state of Connecticut. In 1995, when the destruction of the forest peaked, 11,200 square miles (29,000 sq. km) of rain forest were lost to cattle pastures and soybean farms; which released 370 million tons of greenhouse gases into the atmosphere, or nearly 5 percent of the world's total! Since 1970, over 250,000 square miles (647,500 sq. km) of forest has been destroyed – an area almost as large as Texas. Over 90% of the land deforested since 1970 is used for cattle pastures, while the rest grows soya. As a result, Brazil has become the world's leading producer of beef, and second largest for soybeans.

Even though this continuous loss of rainforest is horrendous, the government of Brazil reported in September 2006 that 2005 figures represent an 11% decrease over the year before. Unfortunately what this decrease really means is that the amount of rain forest available continues to decrease.

Most of the soybeans produced in the Amazon are sent to Europe to provide feed for chickens and cattle. Most soya production in the Amazon is illegal because environmental regulations require Amazon landowners to set aside 80 percent of their lands as undisturbed forest.

Imagine the collateral environmental destruction this deforestation causes once heavy rains start stripping the land of its topsoil during heavy rains, or when vast fires rage out of control. Now consider that this IS already occurring in Brazil, where an average rainfall of 9 feet (108 inches or 274 cm.) assaults hillsides and mountains each year, sending priceless topsoil downstream! It doesn't take much imagination to think of the massive amount of rich organic topsoil disappearing. But how might these distant events affect those of us who live far from the Amazon?

The Amazon River

The Amazon River is over 4,000 miles (6,400 km) long and carries approximately 20% of the fresh water discharged into the oceans, by far more water than any river in the world. The Amazon River collects water from Bolivia, Ecuador, Peru, Colombia, French Guiana, Suriname, Guyana, Venezuela, and throughout Brazil. Forty percent of the water discharged by South America into the Atlantic Ocean finds its way into the Amazon River.

Even more remarkable is the fact that *28 billion* gallons of water flow into the Atlantic Ocean from the Amazon River every MINUTE. This immense discharge is so great that it dilutes the salinity of the ocean for more than 100 miles from the mouth of the Amazon. The Amazon River is so long and wide that a boat can navigate it inland from the sea for over 2,300 miles, roughly the distance between Los Angeles to Savannah, Georgia. At the height of the rainy season at its estuary the river is over 200 miles (325 km) wide at its mouth.

This watershed covers half of Brazil and is home to the world's greatest biodiversity. The Amazonian rain forest lies within the lowlands of the Amazon basin, stretching from the Andes in the west to the Atlantic Ocean on the east. Because its vegetation continuously recycles carbon dioxide into oxygen this forest has been described as the "lungs of our planet." But unlike our lungs which discharge carbon dioxide and take in oxygen, this massive rainforest takes in carbon and discharges oxygen, exactly what is needed when the Earth is facing global warming. Loss of the Amazon watershed could have a catastrophic effect on the entire world's climate, especially as more and more fossil fuel and methane is released into the atmosphere.

Fifty percent of the rainfall on the Amazon returns to the atmosphere via evaporation by the forest's dense foliage. Imagine how many countries in the world would lose significant amounts of rain needed to grow food, if this Amazonian cycle of rainfall and evaporation declines. As more and more countries, particularly in Africa, feel the effect of the Amazon's destruction, what will Africans do to obtain water needed for crops?

In addition, over 500 mammals, nearly 500 reptiles, and one fifth of the world's birds live in the Amazon basin. Biologists estimate that nearly 2.5 million different insect species make their home there, including over 300,000 different beetles. The total number of separate botanical species that exist in the Amazon is still unknown. Estimates are there are tens of thousands, not counting the extraordinary variety of fungi, mosses, and lichens yet to be identified. Biologists estimate that in just one square kilometer (247 acres) of the Amazon basin, over 75,000 species of trees and over 150,000 species of higher plants exist, or 90,000 tons of living plants.

One fifth of the Amazon River drainage basin area has already been deforested. To date, this vast tropical forest has provided us hundreds of plants that have led to the development of over 150 drugs in use today. How many more life-saving botanicals or living organisms are there yet to be discovered? Could one of them be right underneath an açaí palm?

This amazingly complex, diverse and bewildering Amazonian basin is where the story of the açaí pulp and its attributes starts – a fruit whose antioxidant activity is superior to that of almost any fruit or vegetable in the world.

Chapter 4
The Açai Berry

Historical Evidence for the Use of Açai Berries as a Food

Everything that is "natural" is not necessarily safe to consume. Can we eat it every day? Can one be allergic to it? Can pregnant or breastfeeding women consume it? Is it sprayed with any chemicals that might damage our nervous system or cause cancer? Hence, information about the traditional use of a food and consumption patterns can give us a lot of information of its' safety as a food.

There are two ways to determine food safety. One approach is to conduct toxicology studies that demonstrate safety, thereby providing scientific evidence it's safety. A second approach is to document historical use of the food.

Earliest British Recording of Açai

In early 1768, Captain James Cook received funding from England's Royal Academy and the British Navy to sail to the South Pacific and observe the transit of the planet Venus across the face of the sun. The purpose of the voyage was to measure the distance between the sun and earth and the size of the solar system. Astronomers determined that this event would transpire on June 3, 1769.

As they were preparing to leave England in August 1768, he and his crew were asked by the Royal Society to explore *Terra Australis Incognita*, the mythical southern continent. At the time, it was believed that there was a large unexplored continent somewhere in the southern hemisphere. It was customary during voyages of discovery to include naturalists with botany training to record what was found.

Joining them on this voyage of inquiry was Joseph Banks (1743-1820), a botanist, who would eventually become regarded as one of the greatest botanists in history. Capt. Cook and his crew of 80 men and 11 scientists, including Joseph Banks, left England on August 26,1768 on the ship *H.M.S. Endeavor*. After stopping in the Madeira Islands and sailing the west coast of Africa, the ship headed across the Atlantic to South America. The ship's first stop was Brazil, arriving on November 13, 1768.

The *H.M.S. Endeavor* was a 106 feet long collier, a ship with a shallow draft and flat bottom that could get close to shore and withstand running aground. The design of the ship also allowed the *Endeavor* to sail along a coastline and send a group to explore the shore and go inland.

While in Brazil, Joseph Banks had the benefit of two other botanists on the *Endeavor*, Daniel Solander and Herman Spöring, Solander's assistant. Solander was a student of Linnaeus, "the Father of Taxonomy." Linneaus' system for naming, ranking, and classifying organisms is still in wide use today. The three of them had the opportunity to describe and discover all kinds of plants and animals never reported before. As Banks put it, his job was "to record all manner of plant and animal life encountered." Banks made the first scientific description of a now common garden plant, bougainvillea (named after Cook's French counterpart, Louis-Antoine de Bougainville). Banks kept meticulous records of his observations in a journal from the date he left England on the *Endeavor* until he returned to England on July 31, 1771, three years later.

The botanists on board the Endeavor were also interested in what foods natives consumed. In an entry in his journal on December 7, 1768, Joseph Banks mentions the açaí fruit as a food eaten by natives. He described açaí as follows: *"Palm berries [that] appear much like black grapes but for eating have scarce any pulp covering a very large stone."* Quite an accurate description of the fruit!

After a brief stay in Rio, the *H.M.S. Endeavor* proceeded west to Tahiti to build an observatory. Once built, Charles Green, who worked at the Greenwich Observatory in England and who was a passenger on the Endeavor, measured the transit of Venus across the Sun. Once this task had been accomplished, the Endeavor sailed southwest until it reached New Zealand and the east coast of Australia, whose coastline had not been mapped.

Earliest Portuguese Accounting of Açai Harvesting

The Portuguese University of Coimbra's Department of Anthropology is famous for a remarkable collection of Amazonian masks gathered by Portuguese explorers of the 18th and 19th century, as well as a fine collection of old books and manuscripts related to the exploration of "new worlds."

During a visit to Portugal, I met with a professor of anthropology at the University. My mission was to locate historical documents related to the use of açaí in Brazil. Fortunately, she had a remarkable memory for what was stored on the shelves of the anthropology department's collection, including that of a very large book that included numerous drawings made by a Portuguese naturalist who explored the eastern Amazon flood plains where vast stands of açaí palms grow.

While we were walking to the library, I mentioned my interest in the açaí palm and its fruit. This narrowed our search, and without hesitation, the professor located an oversized book that contained color drawings of birds, fish, amphibians, reptiles, insects, plants and natives, drawn by artists that were members of a 1791 expedition into the Amazon. After putting on a pair of white gloves, the professor took the book of interest from its shelf and laid it on one of the library's tables. Soon others in the library joined us as the professor carefully opened it.

After marveling at the color drawings of birds, fish, and other creatures seen by the artist, we came upon drawings of natives living along some tributaries of the Amazon River. In the background of a drawing that caught my attention was a native holding small black berries in one hand, with a basket by his feet, with the distinctive açai palm trees in the background. Here I was in one of the oldest universities in the world, looking at a drawing over two hundred years old, showing Amazonian natives collecting açai fruit in baskets, much the same way it's done today!

Before leaving the university, arrangements where made to photocopy this drawing shown in Figure 3.

Figure 3

Earliest American Recording of Açai

At the close of the American Civil War, William H. Edwards, a renowned entomologist, naturalist, and explorer, wrote a book about his travels into the Amazon basin in 1846.

A trained observer, Edwards made many contributions to our understanding of the Amazon and its people, including their diet. Soon after Edwards came back from the Amazon, English scientists Henry Bates and Alfred Wallace, who contributed further to our knowledge of the Amazon in the 19th century, followed him.

In chapter four of his book, *Voyage Up the River Amazon, Including a Residence in Para in 1846,* Edwards reports on a most "delightful" fruit he called "assai." Having not seen this palm before coming to the Amazon, he unfortunately mistook it to be the related palm, *Euterpe edulis,* well known by that time. It was found in great abundance south of Sao Paolo where the largest concentration of Brazilians resided, along with that of the growing populations that lived in Rio de Janeiro and the capital of Brazil at the time, Salvador, both located on the Atlantic coast.

Availability of Açai Fruit

The açai palm grows throughout the Amazon, the densest concentration found in lowland flood plains where large groves of açai palms grow. In many areas of the Amazon, particularly in the eastern drainage basin, the dense clusters of açai palm trees that number in the millions provide the canopy of the rainforest, shading everything under its fronds from the sun's ultraviolet light. Over millions of years the açai palm has adapted to the sun's ultraviolet radiation, but only after maturity and is able to produce fruit. Until the palm gets past the juvenile stage it needs shelter from the sun just like many of the plants that grow in the Amazon.

Açai is known by many other names. There are at least 18 synonyms for the fruit depending on where you live in the Southern Hemisphere. Besides being called the "cabbage palm", synonyms for açai include:

Brazil:	*Açai, acal, açaizerio, assai, jicara, jussara, jucara and palmiteiro.*
Trinidad:	*Manac.*
Suriname:	*Manaca or manaka.*
Colombia:	*Naidi.*
French Guiana:	*Pinapalm, piria and pinot.*

In addition, tribes around the Amazon have adopted their own names for the fruit, including: *prasara, wapoe, wasei,* and *wipi.* However, "açai" is by far the most popular name for this fruit. In areas where the palm tree grows in vast numbers around the Amazon River and its tributaries, far from large cities and towns, every part of the palm, not just the fruit is utilized.

Açai was not always that well known. There was a time, not so long ago, when very few people outside of the Amazon basin or around Brazil's Atlantic Forests knew much about this fruit. One of the reasons was obtaining access.

More than 50 years ago, travel in and out of the Amazon was difficult, to say the least. Roads were unreliable and rail service was limited or nonexistent. As a result, açai was not seen far from its growing regions.

Once the fruit is picked it quickly deteriorates (as just about every plant does in the tropics). When a plant or plant part reaches maturity or drops to the ground, numerous creatures seek it out, or numerous enzymes are released which break it down. Only by significantly slowing down enzymatic reactions that begin after the fruit is harvested can its nutritional value and antioxidant activity be fully preserved.

By the 1990's an effective transportation infrastructure reached many areas of the Amazon. Modern food processing facilities also sprung up to process the bounty of the Amazon, particularly in and around the city of Belém, the largest city in the state of Pará, within five degrees of the equator. Belém is situated 100 miles (160 kilometers) south of the Equator on the Baía de Marajó, the estuary of the Rio Tocantins and the Rio do Pará. The city is the capital of the state of Pará. The Rio Tocantins and Rio do Pará rivers are part of the Amazon River system.

With a population of over 1.3 million inhabitants, Belém do Pará, as Brazilians refer to it, is the major commercial center of northern Brazil. Belém is a city known for its mango trees (*Mangifera indica*), which is why locals call Belém the *Cidade das Manguerias*. The city has a remarkable amount of river traffic. The bounty of foods growing and produced in the Amazon get consolidated and shipped to major cities in Brazil, such as Rio de Janeiro and Sao Paolo, or to markets around the world.

Citizens of Belém purchase an average of 250,000 liters of açai juice each day during the dry season when açai is harvested, not only from the vendors who sell it but from açai palms that grow in backyards and public lands. Because they live in the Amazon, they are able to consume the juice fresh, especially at lunch when vendors offer a variety of thick, medium, or diluted açai juices. To meet this insatiable daily demand for the "purple juice", over 35,000 people work in the açai industry in Belém.

According to a press release of December 11, 2007, the Brazilian Ministry of Agriculture (*Ministerio do Planejamento*) reported that açai has become Para state's top non-wood product. The North Region of Brazil in the heart of the Amazon, where Para state is located, was responsible for 90.7% of the national production of açai. In 2006, 101,341 tons of açai was collected nationally, with Para state providing 87.4%.

Interestingly, as the production of açai has increased, the production of heart-of-palm has decreased. Heart-of-palm production in 2006 was 17% less than in 2005, of which 92.8% came from Para state. Some of the heart-of-palm is harvested from old açai palm trees that are no longer safe to climb or have diminished fruit yield. These old palm trees can yield over 25 pounds of palm heart (called "palmito").

In Para state, Belém is to açai, what oranges are to Florida, but on a scale that has to be experienced. As midnight approaches hundreds of watercrafts arrive from all over the region landing at the famous *Feira do Açai* market in Belém's *Vero-o-Peso* district. This marketplace supports over a hundred vendors who sell between 550,000 pounds (250,000 kilos) to over a million pounds of açai fruit from roughly midnight to 4 a.m. This activity, on a smaller scale, occurs throughout the eastern Amazon basin wherever a concentration of communities exist within reasonable proximity of riverside towns and cities eager to purchase the day's harvest of açai fruit. As the sun begins to rise brokers and wholesales have sold every last basket of fruit to retail vendors and commercial processors. By early morning the fruit is being macerated all over the region to produce fresh açai pulp juice (*vinho de açai*) for eager consumers, or turned into frozen pulp. Just look for the red "Açai" signs – impossible to miss anywhere you travel in Belém during the harvest season.

Management of Açai Palms

There are over 15,500 square miles (25,000 sq. km) of floodplain forests (called *várzea*) in the Amazon estuary that covers 6,200 square miles (10,000 sq. km) dominated by açai palms, extending from the mouth of the Xingu River to the convergence of the Amazon and Para rivers at Marajo Island. Brazilians refer to this Amazon estuary as the *Marajó várzea ecoregion*.

Local management of açai is evident wherever one goes - particularly along the channels and shorelines in the Amazon basin, where dense stands of old açai palms, called "*terreiros*", are found growing around homes and gardens. Although açai palms dominate these home garden stands and provide much needed shade, typical gardens also grow lemons, cacao and mangoes.

When an açai palm gets old, it is best to remove it to encourage re-sprouting around the dead trunk. It normally takes about 12-13 years for the re-sprouted area to yield fruit for harvesting. Another reason to remove older palms as mentioned earlier is the possibility that it make break when climbing resulting in serious injury, even death.

Studies of fruit production have shown that the açai palm needs direct light to produce a bountiful amount of fruit. However, many producers have learned that giving the palm light shade will actually increase the quality and quantity of fruit pulp.

These studies are also finding ways in which both açai fruit and hearts-of-palm can be harvested without damaging biodiversity. This means that as demand for açai increases, plantations rich in açai palms, called *açaizais*, can be created that will respect the need to maintain biodiversity and sustainability and at the same time meet export needs. The Brazilian government is now committing personnel and resources to help landowners learn how best to work their land to produce sustainable harvests. For example, agricultural specialists are advising those managing *açaizais* to only harvest heart-of-palm once every five years, without upsetting the ecological balance desired to maintain biodiversity.

Just how important the commercial value of açai fruit has become to the economy of Para state is shown in the pie chart in Figure 4.

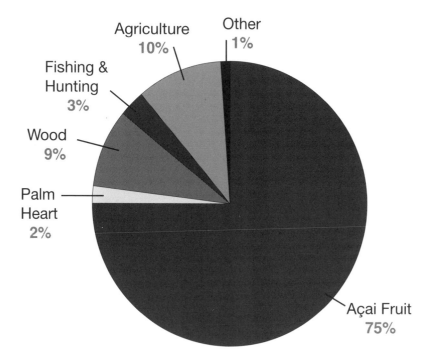

Figure 4: Percentage of Agricultural Products Produced in Para State

Source: Mochiutti S. *Potencial de producao de fructose de Açai em Acaizais manejados no estuaries Amazonico*. Provided by the Department of Agriculture (Embrapa), Amapa, Brazil, 2007.

Chapter 5

Popularity of the Açai Berry

There are many accounts as to how açai popularity gained prominence. Here was a fruit known to natives since antiquity, but only became familiar to Brazilians in the last two decades. In 1995, when my interest in the fruit began, it was barely known outside of South America.

Brazilians love to dance, whether the lambada, batuque, capoeira, samba endredo, samba reggae, rainha da bateria, forro, frevo, carimbo, maxixe, congada, kankukus, cordoes, passista, choro, xango, yurupari, maracatu, or the modinha, a sentimental dance derived from Portuguese songs.

One myth has it that a group of capoeira dancers from Rio de Janerio spread word that if they drank açai they could dance for hours. Capoeira is a martial arts dance style developed by slaves to teach defensive tactics.

Brazilians have also claimed açai is an aphrodisiac, but experimental evidence based on placebo-controlled studies have yet to substantiate this claim.

The real story behind the popularity of açai starts with Carlos Gracie, the great-grandson of a Scottish immigrant to Brazil. Born in Brazil in 1902, he became obsessed with martial arts as a teenager. When he arrived in Rio de Janeiro in 1922 to open a jujitsu academy, he came across a shop near his Copacabana home that imported frozen açai from the Amazon. Based on what he learned about the fruit from this shopkeeper, he encouraged his martial arts students to consume it. As the accomplishments of his students became known people began to wonder what the magic potion was that his students were drinking. Eventually the surfing community in Rio de Janeiro got wind it was açai and before long every juice bar on the beach offered it.

Until 2000, no one imported significant amounts of açai into the United States or other countries around the world, so interest in this "superfood" languished until the beginning of the 21st century.

Some companies promoted and marketed açai products in the early 2000's via distribution in juice bars and mass-market outlets. One such company is Sambozan, based in California, and started by two college-aged students who had traveled to Brazil. These products used spray-dried or frozen açai, which as you will learn later in this book has significantly less of the nutritional and phytochemical composition, and antioxidant activity, of freeze-dried açai, which locks in these components. This may explain why despite being one of the first to market açai products in the United States, it did not see the growth that a late starter such as Monavie experienced, which started marketing its açai based juice in January 2005, and grew 5,883% in its first three years, with revenues approaching one billion dollars, according to *INC* magazine's 500/5000 2009 rankings. Monavie is the largest buyer of açai in the world today, distributing its products in 15 countries around the world, *including Brazil.*

Brazilians also love sports, particularly soccer. Many games are played late at night when the temperature is milder and the sun has set. Athletes participating in such sports consume a glass of açai mixed with other fruits such as guarana (*Paulinia cupana*), which contains around three times as much caffeine as found in the coffee bean. Guarana is commonly added to many sweetened juices or carbonated beverages in Brazil.

Demand for açai surged in recent years, bringing with it the attention of the media, nutritionists and health care practitioners around the world. It also brought the attention of unscrupulous companies engaged in consumer fraud by offering free samples to obtain credit card numbers on the promise of remarkable weight loss. At the end of the book, in the Note section, information is provided on these companies and their unlawful activities based on civil complaints and charges filed by state attorney generals.

More than anything, the media has played a major role in the growing popularity of açai. Here is a sample of quotations about açai that have appeared in various prominent publications in recent years:

"...twice the antioxidants of blueberries and a taste like blackberries crossed with chocolate."

TIME magazine, February 14, 2005

"Rich in antioxidants and amino acids, açai is thought to be one of the most nutritional fruits of the Amazon basin."

New York Times, August 4, 2004

"For those put off by juiced wheatgrass and bored with low-carb bars, there is açai. Açai...the purplish fruit of the palmberry plant, purportedly contains more antioxidants than red wine and has a beguiling berry- like flavor with intense chocolate overtones."

The Washington Post, August 11, 2004

"The latest look-better, live-longer superfood? It's the açai fruit. It's what Denise Richards swears by; what Kelly Slater downs before surfing competition. It's açai, a multipurpose megabooster berry that Hollywood has been hooked on."

People Magazine, January 30, 2006

"Wheatgrass, protein shakes-so 2002. At juicebars and health stores around the country, the hip new taste is açai. Açai...packed with anthocyanins, the same antioxidants that give red wine its health benefits."
The Wall Street Journal, April 18, 2003

"Açai is the fruit of an Amazonian palm tree with the nutritional content that makes other fruits blush with inadequacy."
The London Times, September 20, 2003

In 2004, Dr. Nicholas Perricone, MD, author of *The Perricone Promise*, appeared on the Oprah Winfrey Show, where he told Oprah that açai is his number one choice as a "superfood", because it was "packed full of antioxidants, amino acids and essential fatty acids." Unfortunately, this led to unscrupulous marketers claiming that she endorsed the product, which is not true. (See the Note section before the reference section at the end of the book to learn more about celebrity endorsements.)

National television news shows also gave açai coverage. For example, NBC-TV's *The Today Show*, reported that, "The Anomabi Indians have believed for centuries that açai holds unique power...and is believed to help women after birth and to give anyone who drinks it a burst of energy."

Until our research group published two papers in 2006 in the *Journal of Agricultural and Food Chemistry* as well as another group based at Texas A & M University led by Pozo-Insfran and colleagues, there existed very little information in the peer reviewed scientific literature about açai.

Açai Juices in the Marketplace

Over the last several years many açai-based juices have appeared in the market place.

The flavor of açai is not sweet. Instead it has an earthy taste that leaves a chalky mouthfeel. The texture is thick, requiring a spoon to eat. This explains why despite all of the interest in açai pulp and its antioxidant properties, a pure açai pulp beverage is unlikely to be found in markets outside of the Amazon. In cities like Belém in Pará state, where tons of the fruit arrive freshly harvested every day during the dry season, açai is processed into a juice within hours of arrival due to its perishable nature.

In large towns and cities along the river and estuaries of the eastern Amazon delta, residents mix fresh açai with *farinha* (manioc flour), another staple food, which is made from the cassava root (*Manihot esculenta*). Cassava is particularly suitable to soils with low fertility and acidity and has been a subsistence food for humans living in the Amazon since at least prehistoric times.

Given the need to make açai pulp palatable to the taste buds of other cultures, every açai-based juice product offered outside of the Amazon includes sweeteners and/or other fruits and berries to improve its taste. However, some added ingredients are far better than others in terms of what they contribute to the nutritional value of the juice. Adding ingredients with known antioxidant properties certainly makes more sense than just adding high corn syrup, fructose or sucrose.

When buying açai, local residents are very picky about how old the fruit is and the quality of the pulp. They expect it to be harvested within hours of being offered for sale. After a day, the taste of the pulp changes, and so does its antioxidant capacity. This was the reason so much time was spent trying to figure out how to get this fruit from the field into the laboratory without losing its nutritional and phytochemical composition or antioxidant and organoleptic (taste, appearance, etc.) properties.

Freeze-drying the fruit right in the Amazon proved the best way to preserve the fruit's pulp for research purposes.

Of significant importance is what juice manufacturers do to the fruit's pulp. Açai pulp is very rich in both soluble and insoluble fibers that can leave a substantial residue at the bottom of a bottle if left standing. The typical consumer will wonder what that "stuff" is. The insoluble fiber contains antioxidant polyphenols in the fiber's cell walls.

The pulp is also unusually rich in mono- and poly-unsaturated fatty acids. These are the "good" fats we have heard so much about in recent years. Any açai-based juice with sufficient açai pulp in the product that has not been filtered and clarified will result in a yellowish-green layer of these fats floating at the top. This explains why so many companies filter and clarify the juice to avoid having to take back the product because it has "some strange looking oil floating on top and sediment at the bottom." The leading açai-based beverage in the world (Monavie®), whose predominant ingredient is both freeze-dried and frozen açai pulp, is not clarified or filtered.

The wisdom of leaving the pulp alone and not clarifying it is supported by a pharmacokinetic study conducted in humans authored by Mertens-Talcott and colleagues at Texas A & M University, the University of Florida and the University of Tennessee. In their study, healthy adults either received açai pulp that was clarified or not, and compared to applesauce or a non-antioxidant beverage, which served as controls. The study revealed "açai pulp caused a significant increase in the antioxidant capacity of plasma, which indicates *in vivo* [in the body] the antioxidant potential of açai." The amount of anthocyanins in unclarified açai juice was 145 mg, whereas in clarified juice it was 110 mg. This showed that clarifying the pulp reduced the amount of key polyphenol compounds found in the pulp.

The take home message from this study is that clarifying açai pulp, as many açai-based juices do, reduces its value as an antioxidant-rich food.

Recent Studies on Açai-based Juice

As we age, maintaining joint motion and reducing the painful inflammation associated with limited mobility becomes important to us. So what options do we have to mitigate this problem associated with aging? There is always the option of taking a drug, but what if a food could work just as well and possibly even better without side effects?

In 2009, Honzel and colleagues provided the first experimental evidence that an açai-based juice product sold as a functional food could provide health benefits associated with aging. This pilot study found that the potent anti-inflammatory properties found in freeze-dried açai that were seen in the laboratory (*in vitro*, meaning out of the body) whose results were published in 2006, showed the same effect in humans in the body (*in vivo*).

The study was funded in 2008 by Monavie LLC, and performed by an independent lab selected by a contract research organization. The investigators tested their açai-based juice beverage (Monavie Active®) whose primary ingredient was freeze-dried and frozen açai pulp. They wanted to see if drinking two ounces of the juice twice a day, as recommended on the label, every day for 12-weeks would have any effect on inflammation based on analysis of the subject's blood or result in an improvement in their range of motion of key joints, including the lower lack of the spine. An institutional board for human experimentation approved the study.

Following screening by a physician and interviews, 14 volunteers, 44 to 84 years of age, qualified to participate in the study. Evaluation of their progress involved collecting baseline data from each subject (before the study began) and repeating the same tests at 2, 4, 8 and 12 weeks, including: blood samples, structured nurse interviews, an assessment of pain perception, and logs of daily activities. In addition, subjects were given a range of motion (ROM) assessment using computer-assisted dual digital inclinometry per American Medical Association (AMA) guidelines. The subjects did not know the brand of the product they were consuming, only that it was a fruit juice.

Analysis of the data showed that consumption of the juice over 12 weeks resulted in significant reduction in pain ($p<0.01$), improvement in range of motion ($p<0.05$), and improvement in the range of daily activities ($p>0.025$). Serum antioxidant status, according to a cell-based antioxidant protection assay in erythrocytes, showed significant improvement just two weeks after the study started ($p>0.05$), and continued to improve every two weeks throughout the 12 weeks of the study ($p<0.0001$). A mild decrease in lipid peroxidation and reduction in the inflammatory marker, C-reactive protein (CRP), was also observed. The significant association between improved range of motion, antioxidant status, and pain reduction observed in this study is preliminary in nature, but encouraging.

The study also yielded some surprising findings. Besides increased range of motion, participants reported other improvements. For example, one of the volunteers mentioned that by the eighth week of the study they no longer had to get up during the night to urinate, helping them sleep better and feel more rested. Another volunteer was able to stop pain medication they had been taking for pain in both knees. One subject reported that by the twelfth week not only did they have more energy and fewer aches and pains, but their seasonal allergies and asthmatic attacks had abated. The results of this study was published in *Alternative Therapies in Health and Medicine* in 2009 by this author and colleagues, as part of a discussion on the progress of systematic and collaborative research on açai, and reported at two international scientific meetings during 2008 and 2009.

This is a very small pilot study and the results need replication. A request for funding to perform a larger randomized double-blind, placebo-controlled, clinical trial of longer duration is being submitted. Nevertheless, the pilot study is encouraging as it demonstrated that drinking this açai-based juice, according to the manufacturer's directions, increased antioxidant protection in human cells that correlated with a range of significant benefits experienced by the study's participants.

Unlike the range of motion study, which was a clinical trial without a control group, another study led by Jensen and colleagues, published in the *Journal of Agricultural and Food Chemistry* in 2008, used a more objective clinical trial method, preferred by the scientific community to scientifically evaluate the biological effects of food or drugs in humans: the randomized, double-blind, placebo-controlled, crossover design.

The basis for this second study came about after researchers began analyzing data from another human study that was conducted in 2007 and 2008 that looked at the degree to which açai pulp could protect human cells from oxidative stress. In this study by Jensen and a different group of colleagues, also published in the *Journal of Agricultural and Food Chemistry* in 2008, they found that açai protected cells at a wide range of doses while possessing strong anti-inflammatory properties *in vivo* [in the body]. Using the controlled clinical trial design described above, Jensen and colleagues went on to show that consumption of 4 ounces a day of Monavie Active® juice resulted in a statistically significant improvement of serum blood antioxidant status within two hours after consumption that correlated with a significant inhibition of lipid peroxidation.

Lipid peroxidation refers to the oxidation of fats. The formation of peroxides results in the destruction of the original fat, usually the "good" unsaturated fatty acids, and can lead to the loss of integrity of the membranes that contain these fats. These lipids are the backbone of nerve cell membranes. If chronic production of free radicals causes lipid peroxides to form it can lead to neurological damage. In time, this toxic effect contributes to a pathological process in the body that can lead to the development of neurological diseases. At least that is what we believe based on experimental evidence.

Lipid peroxides have been identified among the factors that contribute to the formation of atherosclerotic plaque in the arterial wall. Research by Niculescu and colleagues, reported in 2007, found a correlation between the content of antioxidant constituents in the serum and the gravity of atherosclerosis. Using the TRAP assay, an antioxidant assay, the researchers found that individuals who had acute myocardial infarctions had low TRAP scores. A low score means poor antioxidant capacity of the serum to deal with oxidative stress that can lead to the formation of lipid peroxides. When a myocardial infarct occurs, heart tissue can be destroyed due to an obstruction of blood supply to the heart muscle, a life-threatening situation. This event is commonly called a heart attack, the leading cause of premature death. The same correlation was found using the TRAP assay in studies done with animals.

Certain diagnostic tests are available to quantify the end product of lipid peroxidation. The most commonly used test is the thiobarbituric acid reactive species assay, usually referred to as the TBARS assay. Thiobarbituric acid is a compound used as a reagent in assaying malondialdehyde, the end product of lipid peroxidation. In the study to be reviewed below, the researchers included the TBARS assay in their randomized double blind, placebo-controlled, crossover study. The reason for the addition of a crossover component in the study is that this allows the investigators to see how the same subject responds to the test item (in this case the açai-based juice) and the placebo. In this way, the subject becomes their own control, which allows for an additional layer of statistical analysis that can be performed in addition to the statistical comparison between different subjects.

The chain reaction that leads to lipid peroxidation can be stopped in the body in several ways. One approach is by using enzymes that are naturally produced in the body, including superoxide dismutase (SOD), catalase, and peroxidases. Two of these enzymes are particularly important in the brain as the way this organ deals with reactive oxygen species (free radicals) is very different from how the rest of the body handles free radicals.

Using antioxidants derived from the diet is another way the body copes with excessive production of free radicals. This is why making sound dietary choices that include numerous fruits, vegetables, whole grains, and nuts, is important. Phytochemicals called anthocyanins found in certain antioxidant-rich foods such as açai, blueberries, cranberries, and raspberries, are compounds that meet our need for dietary sources of antioxidants. So are vitamin E and C, both important antioxidants.

Several antioxidant assays have been developed based on a vitamin E analogue called "Trolox." The most popular assay used by food scientists in the last decade is the oxygen radical absorbance capacity (ORAC) assay. In this assay, a lab technician can quantify the degree to which a food stops the most common free radical found in the body, the peroxyl radical, in terms of units of quenching capacity. When this quenching ability to stop the free radical chain reaction is measured in a laboratory (*in vitro*), the result is reported as so many micrograms of Trolox equivalents per gram. Until açai's antioxidant capacity was measured by the ORAC assay, fruits and berries such as cranberries, black raspberries, wild blueberries, and red raspberries, were among the foods reported to have the highest antioxidant scavenging capacity based on the ORAC assay from among nearly 300 common foods assayed by the USDA's Agriculture Research Service.

Another assay using a different method to measure antioxidant capacity that uses Trolox is the Trolox equivalent antioxidant capacity (TEAC) assay. ORAC and TEAC assays, as well as several other antioxidant assays, are discussed in greater detail in chapter 9.

Freeze drying açai pulp does an exceptional job of preserving the nutrients and phytochemicals in the pulp. It has been found to have very strong antioxidant capacity against the peroxyl radical and superoxide radical, as well the other free radicals, the highest of any food beside a few spices that have been tested in the world. But again, these results are based on laboratory assays, which do not prove biological benefits. We'll get back to this point latter.

Since other free radicals are produced in the body, some of which are far more destructive to healthy cells then others, the body must find a way to stop their production once the chain reactions begin and before significant damage occurs to cells. That doesn't mean that free radicals are "bad." Quite the opposite – they are essential weapons used by our body to keep us healthy and prevent infections. For example, free radicals are used by the immune system to kill viruses, bacteria, cancer cells, and other foreign invaders. Free radicals are only a problem when they are overproduced and cause damage to healthy cells. When this occurs and involves reactive oxygen species, we call this "oxidative stress." It is simply an inability of the body to cope with excessive free radical production.

To study these free radicals several other assays have also been developed to measure how well foods might quench them. Two free radicals of considerable interest are the superoxide radical and the hydroxyl radical. The latter is probably the most damaging of all free radicals and is produced by the superoxide radical, while the former is deployed by the immune system to kill invading microorganisms. If overproduction of superoxide can be inhibited it can reduce the production of the hydroxyl radical.

The production of superoxide beyond its use by the immune system is now thought to contribute to a range of diseases, and possibly accelerate aging because of the damage it inflicts on cells; experimental evidence supports this belief. In yeast, the fruit fly (*Drosophila*) and rodents, when the genes that produce the enzyme that deals with superoxide, called superoxide dismutase (SOD) are removed the result is a reduction in lifespan and an increase in the incidence of symptoms and diseases associated with aging (e.g., macular degeneration, cataracts, muscle atrophy, radioactive damage, cancer, etc.). Conversely, when rodents are selected who produce a lot of SOD (referred to as over-expression), they are more resistant to experiencing strokes or heart attacks. This explains why açai is of such interest to scientists studying aging and age-related diseases as we discovered that the pulp has the highest superoxide scavenging capacity *in vitro* of any food tested to date, as reported in the *Journal of Agricultural and Food Chemistry* in 2006.

Our understanding of how these free radicals affect biological systems, based on thousands of published research papers, is why we now have a better idea of what foods should be recommended to support the body's need to obtain antioxidants from foods and contain and control the production of free radicals.

But the problem of determining which foods would benefit us as sources of antioxidants is made difficult by the fact that just because a food shows it can stop free radical production in the laboratory, does not mean it may do the same thing in the body (*in vivo*). That's why we have to test each food to see if it has a biological effect before promising others that it might be of potential benefit to our health beyond its nutritional value. And that is where experimental studies using foods tested in people under controlled conditions come into play.

A paper in 2008 compared various fruit juices for total polyphenol content. The paper had many methodological weaknesses that make repeating the study impossible, and it never made it clear to the reader that the data showed zero correlation between the amount of polyphenols in any of the juices assayed and its biological activity *in vivo*. Simply put, having more polyphenols in a juice wasn't demonstrated to produce a better health benefit. Why is this? My research shows me that quantity is as important as the existence of certain organic compounds in the food. The presence of other compounds often has a synergistic effect with one another. For example, one study done in a lab in Oregon by Jensen and colleagues, observed that when freeze-dried açai was diluted down to a concentration of one-tenth of one part per trillion in water, the incredibly small amount of whatever compounds remained in açai protected human cells when subjected to hydrogen peroxide. Hydrogen peroxide is a free radical the body produces to defend itself against pathogens. Antioxidants control the reactions this radical produces. An inability to control it can lead to cellular damage. Of course we scratched our heads in astonishment when we saw what açai could do at such low concentrations. It told us that whatever was in açai pulp that did this, did so at almost quantitatively undetectable concentrations via some kind of cell signaling mechanism possibly beyond its antioxidant activity. The take home message is this: The quantity of a particular compound is not always that important or relevant.

A study by Saura-Calixto and colleagues reported in 2007 showed that in the Spanish Mediterranean diet, 48% of dietary polyphenols are bioaccessible in the small intestine, while 42% become bioaccessible in the large intestine, where colonies of bacteria break it down into compounds that are hydrolyzed to render them absorbable. Simply reporting on the quality of the polyphenols in a juice isn't necessarily relevant to what would happen once they enter the gastrointestinal tract. It was reported in another study published in 2009 that a considerable amount of açai is locked in the cell walls of the insoluble fraction of the fruit fiber. This means that to get at the antioxidants locked in cell walls of açai our gut needs to break down those barriers so that the polyphenols can be released and absorbed and finally enter into circulation in our body. When whole grains are processed, for example, the concentration of grain antioxidants is drastically reduced during the refining process, suggesting that the phenolic compounds are concentrated in the outermost layers. Sadly, these outer layers, also rich in fiber, are usually removed during processing, significantly decreasing the food's antioxidant value.

So with this background, let's return to the randomized clinical trial that was performed in humans reported by Jensen and colleagues.

The study investigated the *in vitro* and *in vivo* antioxidant and anti-inflammatory properties of the açai-based juice (Monavie Active®). The cell-based antioxidant protection of erythrocytes assay demonstrated that the antioxidants in the juice penetrated and protected cells of human subjects from oxidative damage ($p<0.001$). It also showed that the production of free radicals (reactive oxygen species) was reduced ($p<0.003$), along with a reduction in the following pro-inflammatory compounds: bacterial peptide f-Met-Leu-Phe (fmlp) ($p<0.001$); leukotriene B4 (LTB4) ($p<0.05$); and, the cytokine, interleukin-8 (IL-8) ($p<0.03$). What does all this mean? We speculate that the anti-inflammatory properties of the juice allow normal immune surveillance, so it can do its job while at the same time reducing inflammatory conditions. These results are so differ from the mechanism of action of most anti-inflammatory drugs.

For individuals with one of 80 different autoimmune diseases, such as fibromyalgia, systemic lupus erythematosus, rheumatoid arthritis, sarcoidosis, and psoriasis, the results from this study are encouraging. It found that cells taken from subjects in the study did not stimulate immune activity by increasing it, rather the compounds in the juice, once absorbed, sent signals to the immune system to maintain normal levels while reducing inflammation. This may explain the frequency of reports of the benefits people have seen following consumption of this juice, an area warranting clinical trials.

As more studies appear in the literature, it seems increasingly suggestive that açai exerts antioxidant, anti-inflammatory, and chemopreventive activities by modulating various components of cellular signaling pathways. Various investigations have led to the identification of flavonoids and other dietary antioxidant compounds present in plant foods as bioactive. This is one reason we took an interest in finding out what types of phytochemicals and compounds were in açai. Based on unpublished analytical studies performed at a university, we now know there are at least 3,000 phytochemicals in açai, including many compounds of great interest in terms of the role they may play in human health.

The reason we began to wonder if açai was more than just an exceptional source for antioxidant compounds, but worked by modulating communications between cells (cellular signaling), arose from the failure to explain the anti-inflammatory, antitumor, and cardiovascular benefits observed solely on the basis of the fruit's antioxidant properties. This urged us to research which compounds in açai modulate cellular signaling during inflammation, or act directly as signaling agents. This becomes more important than ever as a growing segment of the health care community is beginning to believe that all diseases involve inflammation of some kind, especially obesity, diabetes, neurological diseases, and metabolic diseases, which have become epidemic in many countries around the world.

The study by Jensen and colleagues is also of interest as over 90 percent of subjects had a decrease in lipid peroxidation by the end of the second hour based on the TBARS assay after consumption of the juice. The difference was particularly striking when comparing results between those subjects who drank 4 ounces of the juice and subjects who consumed the placebo.

Although these study results are more convincing due to the research design used, often referred to as the most rigorous in terms of clinical trials, it is still only one small study. But the results were statistically significant, so they can't be disregarded or dismissed.

Nevertheless, it is encouraging that a company such as Monavie is funding independent research to substantiate the benefit of their functional line of açai-based foods by providing competent and reliable independent research that its products are more than just another fruit juice. Hopefully, studies of açai products will continue to be funded.

Chapter 6
Food Uses of the Açai Berry

Tribal Use in the Amazon

William Balee has written extensively about the Tupi-Guarani-speaking forest dwelling Ka'apor Indians of eastern Amazonia and their culture. The Ka'apor, Guaja, Tembe, and Arawete, are all examples of Amazonian indigenous peoples that esteem the value of açai.

The Ka'apor, who live in the Amazonian state of Maranhao, name, manage, and classify hundreds of plant species found in their habitat. These people are a good example of a culture that has included açai as a integral part of their lives. The fronds of the açai palm are used as thatch to provide shelter, and the fruit for sustenance. The spiny root of the açai palm is used as a grater to scrape off the skin of sweet manioc (cassava root) before it is boiled in a large pot to create a sweet sauce.

The principal fruits of Ka'apor subsistence include the açai fruit, wild cashews (*Anacardium giganteum*), bacaba fruits (*Oenocarpus distichus*), and eight other plant foods. Almost all of these fruits, including açai, are eaten raw, although açai, bacaba, and the piquia fruit (*Caryocar villosum*), are boiled and mixed into a coarse manioc flour, to create a favorite gruel of Ka'apor children.

Almost every day, time is set aside to gather the fruit of the açai palm when it is in season. Gathering of these foods is a task assigned to adults. Balee observed that all Ka'apor fruit gathering is completed at an average of 18 minutes for men and 21 minutes for women. It is also a subsidiary activity to hunting. For example, Balee points out a hunter may stalk a particular game, often near a tree whose ripe fruit might attract the prey. Once the pursuit ends, the hunter begins to harvest fallen fruit and bring it to the village with the carcass of his prey.

Balee also determined, after some ten years of observation, that 80 percent of the Ka'apor energy requirements can be satisfied by a few forest fruits in terms of calories, vitamins, minerals, protein, and fats. This supports observations made by other groups who have studied the dietary habits of indigenous peoples who incorporate açai as a staple food into their diet.

Uses of Açai in the Amazon

Harvesting of açai is a laborious process that begins by locating which trees hold fruit ready for picking and selection (*debulha*). To climb to the top of the palm tree takes skill and strength and usually done by teenagers and young adults. A tool to harvest the fruit without having to climb to the top and risk injury, death, stinging ants, stingless bees, or snakebites, is slowly gaining acceptance in some regions. Few tools are needed to harvest the fruit: a machete or knife, a climbing belt (*peconha*), made of young açai leaves, a plastic sheet or sack, and a basket (*paneiros*). A full basket will weigh around 20 to 25 lbs. Working in groups of three, an average of 3 baskets full of fruit can be gathered. One family I stayed with claimed they made at least $5 or more per hour; given the extremely low cost of living, this is actually quite a good income and can be earned for nearly six months during the season when açai fruit matures. Once enough baskets are filled, they are transported to a central area and taken in a canoe or small-motorized boat to meet a larger motorized boat called a *carregadores*. *Carregadores* can handle up to several hundred baskets, although I saw several larger boats in one region of estuarine islands (*regiao das ilhas*) that could carry up to 2,000 baskets destined for Belem's wholesale market center along the river

When fresh, the pulp is consumed like a thick soup, eaten with a spoon. This soup forms the major and basic part of the diet of many of the inhabitants of the region. Some add granola to it, but the thought of diluting it down to 5% açai pulp with added fruit and Guarana syrup as they do in Sao Paolo or Rio de Janeiro is considered sacrilegious. Those that have been fortunate enough to eat fresh açai agree that it tastes chalky or "earthy." It is understandable why it is mixed with other fruits and sweetened with sugar and/or guarana syrup outside of the Amazon.

In the 1980's, a study into the dietary habits of people living in the Amazon was funded by the U.S. National Academy of Sciences (NAS), and reported by the World Wildlife Fund (WWF). The authors of this report mentioned that, "Those who consume [the açai berry] often appear strong and full of energy…It is loved and desired by the very young and the very old."

The scientists have also observed that following short periods without açai appears to result in a pattern akin to withdrawal symptoms. Soon after eating some of the fruit, their cravings would dissipate. There is even a saying in the region that, "when one is without açai, one feels a lacking or emptiness in the stomach."

Açai forms an important part of the diet in the Amazon. The production of a refreshing juice is the principle use of açai pulp in the Amazon. It is often consumed during breakfast, lunch and dinner. WWF reported that two liters a day was about average for people living in the region. Açai fruit is not a product that is consumed by only the poor, as some have claimed. Rather, it is found in the homes of just about everyone.

There are many ways to prepare açai, but the most basic is to remove the mesocarp (the middle layer of the pericarp, or fruit wall, which is the fleshy and succulent part) from the seed. There are all kinds of stainless steel machines that do this efficiently found available for purchase. The fleshy mass, or pulp, is mashed by hand, and combined with varying amounts of water, to make as thick a liquid as desired. Hence, açai is usually eaten with a spoon, rather than drunk like a juice.

Prices for the different grades and thicknesses of the fruit vary throughout the year, depending on the product's availability. When supplies are low, due to seasonal variations in fruit production, açai must be transported from some distances up river, where more fruit is available. Thus, price variations occur between peak harvest periods. Often the berries are sold in baskets based on a standard measure of açai fruit called a *paneiro* or *rasa*. Depending on the time of year, the cost will very from $4.00 to $13.00 per basket but hover around $8-$10 on most days. Fruit of lesser quality can be purchased for less than $4.00 a basket. Tons of the açai pulp are stored frozen locally, to insure a steady, year round supply. One 80,000 sq feet refrigeration facility I visited kept frozen pulp at a constant minus 17 degrees F. By the end of the harvest season in December, every square foot will be filled with drums of açai pulp and other tropical fruits.

Açai producers and middlemen rank the quality of the fruit on a scale from 1 to 3, based on the pulp's thickness, freshness, and quality.

The most desirable variety of açai liquid is purple in color, called *açai preto*. There is also a yellow type called *açai branco*, the pulp of which has significantly lower antioxidant capacity.

In cooking, açai is often mixed with other foods in the area, including shrimp, fish, manioc flour, biscuits, or combinations thereof. Sometimes it is sweetened with sugar or other fruits. One can find açai on the menu at almost any hotel.

Besides açai's use as a subsistence food, many other food products are made from açai: purple ice cream (*açai preto*), açai milk shakes, mousse, açai chocolates, and even açai cakes.

As mentioned earlier, the seed in the fruit can constitute up to 90% of the berry. Once the seed is removed from the mesocarp (pulp) and skin, it provides food for livestock, particularly pigs. In many households, the seeds are simply thrown into the pigpen as the pulp and skin is being extracted. The seeds can also be composted. After about three months, the composted seeds turn into a rich soil amendment that can be added to vegetable gardens. The seeds are also used to grow new palms. It takes only a few months, in the moist climate of the region, for the seeds to sprout and form new plant seedlings.

The stem branches on which the fruit grows can be used to make brooms and other useful tools and objects.

Once the fruit is removed from the stem it can be used as mulch. This mulch is useful to commercially important plants such as cacao beans (*Theobroma cacao*), a key ingredient in making chocolate.

With the growing popularity of açai, there is a growing appreciation for the palm's value as a source of income.

As mentioned earlier, the harvesting of heart-of-palm means the imminent death of the palm trees such as *E. oleracea*. The short section of the palm heart is cut out of the top of the tree, and taken to commercial facilities to be processed and canned. During processing, the sections are cut into standardized lengths and put into a bath of water, salt and citric acid and then canned. Once sealed, the cans are placed in steaming water to be sterilized before being labeled and shipped. The açai berry, by comparison, is collected over five to seven months each year without threatening the palm's life.

The Brazilian government is well aware of the effect of poaching of palms for heart-of-palm. Recently, the government encouraged extensive plantation production of the palm Pejibaye (*Bactris gasipaes*), which produces quality heart-of-palm sections. Nevertheless, as long as there is a market for heart-of-palm from açai palms, and poachers are willing to kill upwards of 50 palms for a few dollars a day, this practice will continue.

In summary, the açai palm fruit is a significant element in the diet of those who inhabit the floodplains of the Amazon estuary. Conservation efforts and economics favor the use of the fruit, rather than the destruction of the palm to obtain short sections of heart-of-palm.

Fortunately, palm trees are now being grown on plantations, to allow for cultivated sources of heart-of-palm. Hopefully, this change will decrease illegal destruction of palms by poachers or those seeking to remove the palms for other purposes such as cattle ranching. The commercialization of heart-of-palm can co-exist, but only with careful thought to the effects of losing palm trees in this complex Amazonian estuarine ecosystem.

Chapter 7

Nutritional Value of the Açai Berry

The açai contains an abundance of nutrients. Its nutrient content has been studied for many years. The first wave of studies of the fruit began in 1936 and ended in 1948. The second wave of nutritional composition studies began appearing in 1961, and continues to this day. For example, in 2008 a paper by Chin and colleagues confirmed the presence of lignans and other constituents in the fruit, all of which demonstrated antioxidant and cell protective activities.

Early studies focused on the major vitamins and a few minerals, while later investigations reported on other macronutrients, minerals and trace elements, and the fruit's lipid, carbohydrate, and protein composition.

Half-century ago, analytical studies of the nutrient composition of the açai berry led to the discovery that it contained a wide range of vitamins, minerals, trace elements, and macronutrients, able to support human nutritional requirements. Others studying its use in the diet heard many reports from natives in the Amazon that without açai they did not feel as healthy or have as much energy or endurance.

Many of the earlier studies lacked information that would allow scientists to replicate the results they reported in the literature. Further, the açai berry decays so quickly after harvesting so it can only be studied in Brazil, and then only if samples are quickly frozen and delivered to the lab for analysis. This limitation, in particular, contributed to the scientific community showing little interest in the fruit.

However, the introduction of commercial refrigeration in the Amazon and creation of freeze-drying facilities in northern Brazil, resulted in açai and other fruits from that region receiving attention, particularly because these exotic fruits were appearing in markets outside of the Amazon.

University laboratories in Brazil began showing a renewed interest in cash crops from the Amazon such as açai that had significant commercial potential. This interest started in the 1940's. However, when results were reported in the literature the new data did not agree with previous data, raising questions reliability. For example, measurements of the number of kilocalories per 100 grams of açai ranged from a high of 247 (performed in 1977), to a much lower value of 80 (performed in 1948), and the lowest reported value of 66.3 (performed in 1996). These discrepancies were probably due to variations in the analytical methods and the equipment used by different laboratories. Yet it could be due to the palm berries analyzed, when they were harvested, sample preparation, or differences in the analytical equipment.

Reviewing these studies, led to the question of which reference source could be relied upon to provide nutritional information on a label? Another example is potassium, an important electrolyte, found in açai. The published data for açai potassium levels reported values as high as 1185 mg per 100 grams, or as low as 499 mg per 100 grams, a rather significant difference. Obviously, such differences create questions about the reliability of the data.

By the late 1990's, however, highly sophisticated and validated methods were available to food scientists. Also, excellent methods of food preservation, such as freeze-drying, made samples available for scientists to study nutrition profiles and chemistry.

Given the availability of these new technologies, AIBMR Life Sciences in Tacoma, Washington, decided to start from scratch in determining the nutritional composition of açai. Using independent laboratories with considerable expertise in food chemistry, the most modern analytical equipment, and using only official validated methods of analysis published by professional association such as the American Organization of Analytical Chemists (AOAC), their work began in the 1990's. It also allowed independent laboratories worldwide to reproduce their results, by using the same standard samples, reference procedures, and materials.

With the help of institutions, such the U.S. Department of Agriculture (USDA), Agriculture Research Services (ARS), the University of Arkansas in Little Rock, the University of California at Irvine, the National University of Singapore, and various contract research laboratories, such as Brunswick Laboratories and Flora Research Laboratories, careful analysis of multiple freeze-dried samples from the Amazon could be performed over several years, until we were certain of the results.

What jump-started such intense interest in açai was a study on the nutritive value reported in 1945. The study's authors concluded that the pulp of açai was:

> "...*an essentially energetic food, with a caloric value higher than that of milk, and with a content of lipids twice as high... A food of high caloric value [and] content of the minerals, calcium, phosphorous, and iron, suggests nutritional benefits."*

One of the first things noticed about the first freeze-dried sample of açai we obtained from the Amazon was how oily it was, which we thought was strange for a fruit. Second was the remarkable dark purple color of the pulp.

Our first study involved looking at the nutritional composition of several açai samples. Each sample of freeze-dried açai was found to contain the following vitamins and minerals:

Vitamin A (as beta carotene)	Calcium
Vitamin C (as ascorbate ion)	Magnesium
Vitamin E (as d-alpha tocopherol)	Copper
Vitamin D (as cholecalciferol)	Chromium
Vitamin B-1 (as thiamin)	Zinc
Vitamin B-2 (as riboflavin)	Iron
Vitamin B-3 (as niacin/niacinamide)	Sodium
Vitamin B-6 (as pyridoxine)	Manganese
Vitamin B-12 (as cyanocobalamin)	Selenium
Pantothenic acid (as free anion)	Boron
Biotin	Potassium
Folic Acid	Molybdenum
Inositol	Iodine

We also noted that the sodium content is very low, at just 0.25 percent.

Levels of heavy metals were exceedingly low. For example, only 22 parts per billion (a nearly undetectable level) of lead was found on average in our samples. No doubt this remarkably low level of a heavy metal commonly found in industrialized countries was due to the lack of industrial pollution in the Amazon.

We analyzed açai for the presence of amino acids. To our surprise, it contained every essential and even non-essential amino acids needed for protein synthesis.

Alanine	Lysine
Arginine	Methionine
Aspartic acid	Phenylalanine
Cystine	Proline
Glutamic acid	Serine
Glycine	Threonine
Histidine	Tryptophan
Hydroxyproline	Tyrosine
Isoleucine	Valine
Leucine	

Açai pulp provides around 130 calories per one ounce (25 grams) serving, while its dietary fiber content is 44 grams per 100 grams. The fructose, lactose, sucrose, glucose and maltose, content, or total sugars, is one gram per 100 grams of the product, very low for a fruit, hence why it is not sweet tasting.

Açai has a highly desirable quantity of healthy fats, particularly the plant-derived monounsaturated and polyunsaturated fatty acids, which are needed for essential metabolic functions. 82% of açai pulp's fatty acids are composed of monounsaturated and polyunsaturated fatty acids. Oleic acid, a monounsaturated fat, is the most predominant fatty acid in the pulp, followed by palmitic acid. The amount of monounsaturated and polyunsaturated fatty acids is high, in the range of what is found in olives and avocados.

The cholesterol content was reported to be only 1.25 percent. However, due to the assay method, this value represents plant sterols. Cholesterol is almost never found in plants, but closely related sterols are ubiquitous in plants.

The compounds found in açai fruit offer still more benefits. In his 2005 book, *The Perricone Weight-loss Diet*, Dr. Perricone states:

> *"Because of the excellent fatty acid, amino acid, and anti-inflammatory profile, [Açai] deserves star billing. One of the qualities I love about Açai is that it provides us quality protein, healthy fat, and powerful antioxidants, all in one amazing berry."*
> *(pp. 58-59)*

Indeed, açai does contain "healthy fat." It is relatively rich in monounsaturated oleic acid, the primary fatty acid found in olive oil. Oleic acid helps fish oils penetrate cell membranes, providing cells with suppleness and flexibility.

In Dr. Perricone's opinion, açai allows *"all hormones, neurotransmitters, and insulin receptors to function more efficiently; critically important to maintain homeostasis, that is, keeping the body working as it should because all of its systems are in balance."* [p.59]

Only when this balance happens does he believe someone can lose weight and/or reduce the likelihood of gaining unwanted weight.

Dr. Perricone then goes on to explain why he selected açai for his book on weight-loss. *"Açai is good for weight loss because it contains cyanidin, a highly antioxidant phytochemical compound."* He bases this claim on Japanese research that had found evidence that cyanins work by reducing fat absorption and "draining body fat." [p.59] However, there is no experimental evidence using açai to support this claim.

As mentioned earlier, when we obtained freeze-dried samples of açai, we noticed it was oily. This oiliness suggests that açai might contain plant "lipophilic" compounds. Certain biochemical agents are called lipophilic because they are capable of combining with or dissolving lipids (fats).

In 2006, we reported that freeze-dried açai's lipophilic oxygen radical absorbance capacity (ORAC) is the highest of any berry or fruit ever tested. This property means that açai has the potential to inhibit lipid oxidation and thereby reduce the risk of cholesterol being oxidized. A randomized, double-blind, placebo-controlled, crossover study confirmed that when volunteers 18 to 49 years of age consumed an açai-based juice, over 90 percent experienced an inhibition of lipid perioxidation. This study is discussed in greater detail in chapter 9.

For nearly twenty years, it has been important to learn which compounds in foods inhibit oxidation of various biological lipid systems, because these "bad fats" are implicated in the initiation and development of atherosclerosis. Açai's lipophilic antioxidant activity exceeds that of any other fruit or berry, and this intriguing fact may just encourage further research by other research groups.

Our research on the antioxidant activity of the açai berry resulted in a major, significant discovery. We were so excited and impressed that we confirmed our original results by a series of *in vitro* assays. These analytical assays were then repeated a number of times, in different laboratories, using different samples of the freeze-dried fruit, over several years.

To appreciate the significance of our findings, it is important to understand what free radicals are, and how antioxidants work.

Chapter 8

Importance of Antioxidants in the Diet

Public health officials urge consumers to eat several portions of fruits and vegetables every day, to obtain antioxidants. Unfortunately, most people today have little knowledge of what antioxidants are and why they are so important for us.

What is an antioxidant? There are actually many compounds that are collectively called "antioxidants."

A good definition of antioxidant is any substance that retards the body's normal process of oxidation, a reaction to oxygen that releases "free radicals" that damage cells and break the body down. Just breathing air produces free radicals, digestion releases free radicals from food, exercise produces free radicals; we constantly create them. We lose over 30 million cells in the body every minute. In one day it totals over 60 billion cells in a healthy adult. The process of these cells dying is called apotosis and is as natural and essential as breathing. However, in the process of destroying old or dystfunctional cells and replacing them with new functional cells, a lot of free radicals are produced. As long as we can maintain a balance between these radicals and antioxidants, all is well.

Fortunately, our body can quench free radicals to control their ability to damage healthy cells. However, this is not always possible as there is a limit to how many antioxidants the body can produce, and how fast. This is where diet comes in. By insuring that you have ingested foods rich in antioxidants, you are insuring that your body will have antioxidants to cope with excessive production of free radicals.

To understand antioxidants, we first need to learn a little bit about "oxidants." Let's look at oxygen as a good example of an oxidant, also known as an "oxidative substance."

On one hand, oxygen is essential for life, itself. But on the other hand, oxygen can rapidly lead to death, when breathed in excessive quantities for too long. In that case, oxygen becomes toxic.

Oxygen, (actually electrons derived from oxygen) can cause great damage to substances and cells. This destructive process is known as "oxidation" (like rust). Basically, an antioxidant is any substance, even in low concentrations that can significantly delay or prevent this oxidative "rust" damage.

Too high a percentage of oxygen causes the body to age rapidly, basically by rusting internally. Excessive oxygen, chemical compounds containing oxygen, and other substances like hydrogen, cause the formation of unpaired (free) electrons, called "free radicals."

Thinking about the two-edged sword that oxygen delivers will give us another way of looking at free radicals. What we call "rust" is actually the result of unchecked oxygen free radical activity, causing oxidative damage.

Think of free radicals as cattle that are loose and rampaging around fields of planted crops, running wild and causing damage. To prevent such damage, cowboys are hired to round up the stray cattle, watch them and make sure they stay in place and graze peacefully.

Free radicals act just like the stampeding cattle; they move through cells at incredible speeds, potentially damaging millions of healthy, functioning cells. Free radicals cause damage and alterations to cellular DNA that can result in mutated or abnormal cells. The initiation of cancer occurs when a cell's DNA is mutated (or changed). This mutation causes permanent changes in the cell. During the next phase, called the promotion phase, the genetically altered cell is stimulated to repeatedly divide.

Antioxidants act as cowboys herding cattle, by basically rounding up free radicals before they can do much harm. Antioxidants, when available, can bind up free radicals very quickly, before a chain reaction of free radicals causes damage. But if antioxidants are not available, then any damage done by free radicals cannot easily be undone.

To elaborate on the study conducted at the University of Colorado Health Sciences Center in Denver, mentioned in chapter 2, many antioxidants work by terminating the cycle of free radical destruction. These chain-breaking free radical scavengers are referred to as "primary antioxidants." There are other antioxidants, such as oxygen quenchers and synergists that remove oxygen from the auto-oxidation process, or nitrogen quenchers and synergists that protect enzyme systems. However, we are mainly concerned with the free radical quenching ability of antioxidants found in food.

Unless stopped, free radicals can lead to formation of pre-cancerous cells. Cancer development occurs via a series of steps. Oxidative damage involved in this process causes the formation of tumors through several mechanisms.

Mainly, oxidative stress causes DNA damage. Left unrepaired, these DNA alterations lead to point mutations (single- and double-strand breaks), DNA cross-linking, and rearrangement and breakage of chromosomes.

So, in summary, excessive oxygen free radicals are damaging your health when they create a state of oxidative stress. With oxidative stress, the high level of reactive oxygen toxic species (ROTS) overcomes the body's production of antioxidants. At that point, antioxidants from the diet become critical.

In 2005, researchers at Cornell University in New York provided two lists that showed the mechanism of action of many dietary antioxidants.

The first list below shows the possible mechanisms of action of antioxidants that may prevent cardiovascular disease:

Neutralization of free radicals and reduction of oxidative stress while preventing LDL-cholesterol oxidation

Modulation of cholesterol synthesis

Regulation of lipids

Inhibition of cholesterol absorption

Reduction of platelet aggregation

Regulation of nitric oxide production

Lowering of C-reaction protein

Regulation of blood pressure

Regulation of prostaglandin synthesis (PGE-2)

Promotion of the expression of hepatic LDL-cholesterol receptors

Regulation of sterol regulatory element-binding proteins

A second list of mechanisms of action describes the inhibitive, inductive, and promotive properties of dietary antioxidants that may lower the risk of developing cancer:

Neutralization of free radicals and reduction of oxidative stress

Inhibition of abnormal cell proliferation

Induction of abnormal cell differentiation

Inhibition of oncogene expression

Induction of tumor suppressor gene expression

Induction of abnormal cell cycle arrest

Induction of the death of abnormal cells ("apoptosis")

Inhibition of signal transduction pathways

Enzyme inhibition via the phase one enzyme that blocks the activation of carcinogens such as cyclooxygenase-2 (COX-2), nitric oxide synthase (iNOS), and xanthine oxide

Enzyme induction and enhancement of detoxification via the phase 2 enzymes (glutathione peroxidase, catalase, and superoxide dismutase)

Enhancement of immune function and surveillance

Promotion of anti-angiogenesis

Inhibition of abnormal cell adhesion and invasion

Inhibition of nitrosation and nitration

Prevention of DNA binding

Regulation of steroid hormone metabolism

Regulation of estrogen metabolism

Modulation of antibacterial and antiviral substances

Admittedly, one might need an education in molecular biochemistry and medicine to fully appreciate the list of items above. The important point is the recognition based on thousands of published studies that antioxidants exert many different actions, each of which may benefit our health in numerous ways.

Vitamins C and E, for example, are two antioxidants that we derive from eating fruits and vegetables. These vitamins scavenge free radicals that might otherwise cause cell damage that can if left alone and of a chronic nature lead to illness and disease.

Free radicals are often used by the immune system to kill viruses and bacteria, as will be discussed later. However, unless free radicals are neutralized or "quenched" by antioxidants (free radical scavengers), these same free radicals can result in oxidative stress and eventually cause havoc in our body.

Over the years, people have asked me if taking a good dose of vitamin C each day would make up for their failure to eat fruits and vegetables. Based on research reported in 2000 in the journal Nature, my answer is always the same – just taking a large dose of one nutrient will not equal the benefit available from whole foods, such as can be obtained from a variety of fruits, including açai.

The Role of Flavonoids in Food

Flavonoids basically protect plants against stress. Each flavonoid shares a common chemical structure called a phenolic ring. The variations that exist within these phenolic rings can account for the differences between individual flavonoids. To date, more than 4,500 flavonoids have been identified in plants. The flavonoids in the human diet come primarily from foods rich in flavor, color and aroma.

A primary property of flavonoids is their antioxidant value in plant foods. When consumed on a regular basis, foods rich in flavonoids, especially fruits and vegetables, can contribute to our health, by benefiting virtually every system in our body. Its mode of action relates to the ability of flavonoids to modulate communications between cells. We have observed this very behavior while studying açai and an açai-based fruit juice in human cells.

In addition, flavonoids have been described as biological response modifiers, since they can alter the body's response to bacteria, viruses, carcinogens, free radicals, and substances that contribute to inflammation as well as allergens.

The level of flavonoids present in many plants increases during seed and plant development, and helps protect it against environmental stresses, including ultraviolet radiation and insects.

In addition, there is growing evidence that certain flavonoids can contribute to the prevention of some degenerative diseases.

Among the major groups of flavonoids we want in our diet are the following each of which is found in açai:

1) Flavanols. These include the monomers called catechins, and the polymers called proanthocyanidins.

2) Flavonols. These are commonly found in berries.

3) Flavones. These are found in many herbs.

4) Isoflavones. Found in foods like soybeans, members of this group of flavonoids.

5) Flavonals, also called anthocyanidins, are related to anthocyanins found in colorful berries, such as grapes and blackberries.

6) Flavanones. Commonly found in citrus fruits.

In Table 1., on the following page, is a list of some of the many phytochemicals found in açai and in other foods that have been associated with health benefits.

Table 1
Some of the Phytochemicals Identified in Açai.

Anthocyanadin	Gallic acid
Anthocyanin	Homoorietin
Beta-sitosterol	Isoquercitin
Campesterol	Isovitexin
Catechin	Kaempferol
Chyrsoeriol	Luteolin
Coumeric acid	Luteolin-4-glucoside
Cyanidin-3- glucoside	Methyl-derivative
Cyanidin-3-glucoside-coumaraterutinoside	of homoorientin
	Myricetin
Cyanidin 3-O-rutinoside	Orientin
Deoxyhexose	Polyphenols
Ellagic acid	Proanthocyanin
Epi-catechin	Protocatchuric acid
Eriodictyol	Protocatechic acid
Eriodictyol-7-glucoside	Pterostilbene
Eurpatorin	Quercitin-3-arabinoside
Ferulic acid	Resveratrol
Flavanols	Sigmasterol
Flavonoids	Taxifolin
Flavonols	Vanillic acid

The Role of Polyphenols in Food

For the purposes of our discussion of antioxidant activity related to the açai berry, it becomes necessary to introduce the chemical term, polyphenol.

Polyphenols are compounds found in a wide range of plants, particularly, fruit-bearing trees and shrubs. Polyphenols constitute a diverse group of substances that are called polymeric compounds by chemists. Chemists classify them according to their repeating monomeric building blocks. High levels of polyphenols are generally found in fruit skins.

The main classes of plant polyphenolic compounds are flavonoids, lignins, simple phenylpropanoids, and tannins.

To date over 10,000 different plant phenolics have been identified.

Plants produce polyphenols for a variety of functions: antibacterial and antifungal agents, scents that attract insects or birds, feeding deterrents (anti-feedants), signaling molecules that help cells understand what to do, and plant pigments, such as the bright colors of many fruits. Most of us are familiar with the aromatic class of phenolics used as food flavorings: cloves that contain the phenolic compound eugenol; nutmeg – myristicin; and cinnamon, whose distinctive fragrance is due to the phenolic cinnamaldehyde.

Phytoalexins are a class of phenolic compounds very important to plants. They protect plants against fungal and bacterial pathogens. Resveratrol, a stilbene phytoalexin is an example of such a compound as it has strong anti-fungal properties. Isoflavonoids are produced in legumes, such as soybeans, in response to fungal infection. Tannins, another phenolic phytoalexin, inhibit fungal growth in trees.

Polyphenols are of particular interest to humans because many of them have been shown to have strong antioxidant activity, and are anti-inflammatory, anti-bacterial and anti-fungal, and have been shown to rejuvenate the skin and protect it from ultraviolet radiation.

For example, there are certain ultraviolet-absorbing flavonoid phenolics that protect plants against the damaging effect of short wave ultraviolet radiation. Some of the flavonoids that have this ability include quercitin, which is found in most plants, and kaempferol, which is released by plant cells in response to increased ultraviolet B (UV-B) radiation. Once released, kaempferol protects cells from free radicals generated during exposure to UV-B, while reducing the ability of UV-B to penetrate into the mesophyll (skin) cells of the plant.

A surprising number of polyphenols have been identified in açai, including resveratrol, gallocatechins (EGCG), catechin, epicatechin, quercetin, and kaempferol.

Many years ago polyphenols were referred to as Vitamin P. Unfortunately, critics claimed they were non-essential. For this reason research into polyphenols decreased dramatically. It turns out that polyphenols are far more important to our health than we had imagined.

For example, it turned out that certain phenolic compounds are the primary contributors to the antioxidant activity of fruits. Two classes of compounds fall into this category: carotenoids and flavonoids.

Carotenoids, which are oily hydrocarbons, produce yellow, orange, orange/red, and red coloration in fruits and vegetables. By contrast, the flavonoids are water-soluble and produce a much wider variety of colors, from reds and yellows to blues and purples. The main flavonoid that is responsible for these color variations is called an anthocyanin.

Today, these carotenoid and anthocyanin compounds are recognized for their ability to reduce the risk of cardiovascular disease and cancer, although much more research in humans is needed to prove this premise.

During years of research on açai we discovered that this fruit is very rich in polyphenols. The major and minor polyphenols in açai are believed to be largely responsible for the fruit's remarkable antioxidant capacity, including an anthocyanin called "cyanidin-3-rutinoside", which will be discussed later in this chapter.

For those people interested in the pH of açai, it is important to note that a fruit is an alkaline-ash producing food. This means that despite starting off acidic, once digested and metabolized, the fruit makes venous blood more alkaline. Think of what happens in a fireplace. If you burn wood, it will leave ash behind once all of the cells in the wood have been used to produce heat. Food works the same way in our body. We consume foods. Each food will result and turn into an "ash" that is acid or alkaline. In the end, what is important is what the foods ultimate contribution is to the pH in our blood. Studies done by Rudolph Wiley, PhD, and reported in a book called *BioBalance*, led to the discovery that a nearly ideal pH in venous blood should be 7.4, as venous blood is a reflection of the end product of metabolism of everything we eat and what is going on in our bodies.

Anthocyanins are affected by pH. As they become more alkaline the pigment color of the fruit becomes darker, such as the blueness of a blueberry or the dark purple color of açai. But what has puzzled us for years is that açai has one-fifth the anthocyanin content of blueberries, yet it still is many times stronger an antioxidant *in vitro*. This suggests that there are other compounds in açai that contribute to its extraordinary antioxidant capacity. We are currently engaged in research that is leading to the discovery of what those compounds are.

The Role of Proanthocyanidin in Food

Proanthocyanidin is a class of flavonoid also found in plants. Foods containing proanthocyandin include: grapes, bilberry, black currant, green tea, black tea, cranberry, chokeberry, and as we discovered, açai. Technically, the proanthocyanidins in açai are oligomeric proanthocyanidins (OPC's), but that is a mouthful, so we'll just refer to them as proanthocyanidins. OPC's are also found in cranberries and red grapes. Researchers have found that proanthocyanidins can act as free radical scavengers in the human body.

The flavonoids known as "proanthocyanidins" contain a specific type of flavonoid, called a flavanol. As a free radical scavenger, this flavanol is 20 times more powerful than Vitamin C, and approximately 50 times more potent than Vitamin E. While studying the fruit pulp's chemistry, we discovered that this pulp contains several proanthocyanidins as minor constituents, which probably work together, resulting in a synergistic effect that contributes to its strong antioxidant capacity.

Proanthocyanidins have also been shown to reduce the production of histamine, a compound the body produces in response to allergies. In addition, proanthocyanidins can cross the blood brain barrier and protect brain cells, while also protecting the cardiovascular system that delivers vital nutrients to the brain.

The Role of Anthocyanins in Food

Our research on the chemistry of açai firmly established that this fruit is very rich in anthocyanins. The non-flavonoid polymers found in açai, known as anthocyanins, are composed of esters of the polyphenolic monomers. We discovered which anthocyanins were predominant, and which ones are more minor constituents. This research provides scientists information on the quantitative as well as qualitative chemistry of the anthocyanins in açai pulp.

Anthocyanins are found in the fruit's skin; they prevent photo-damage by absorbing blue-green light, and protect the skin from damage by ultraviolet (UV) radiation. Think of anthocyanins as a fruit's sunscreen.

In trying to determine what kind of açai juice should be studied, attempts were made to utilize clarified or semi-clarified açai. However, it quickly became apparent that any clarification or filtering of the juice had an adverse effect on the levels of anthocyanins left after clarification. We measured a loss of nearly 30% of the anthocyanins following clarification and a far greater loss of antioxidant activity. Over 30-days, half of the dominant anthocyanins, including cyanidin-3-glucoside and cyanidin-3-rutinoside, had disappeared. This information helped us determine that for any future study of an açai juice, we had to select a non-clarified and non-filtered açai-based beverage when performing human studies.

Anthocyanins have been demonstrated to scavenge a number of free radicals, including the hydroxyl, peroxyl, and superoxide radicals. All these free radicals can accelerate the rate of aging, and contribute to degenerative diseases, especially disease or conditions involving inflammation (e.g., obesity).

Anthocyanin compounds also benefit the cardiovascular system by inhibiting lipoxygenase and cyclooxygenase enzymes, which are both involved in lipid peroxidation. During lipid peroxidation, lipids break down to form more free radicals. This is the process we call "rancidity." When oil becomes rancid, we refer to the oil as having been ruined by excessive exposure to oxygen. Unless the chain reaction of lipids breaking down because of exposure to oxygen is stopped, the oxidative degradation of lipids continues unabated.

If antioxidants are not available to terminate this reaction, the free radicals will continue to steal electrons from lipids in our cell membranes. Peroxidation results in cell damage, along with further increased production of free radicals. Lipid peroxidation has been implicated in the development of cancer, cardiovascular disease, Alzheimer's disease and Parkinson's disease.

Because of the way polyphenolics work, these anthocyanins may play an important role in maintaining cardiovascular health, which may prevent cardiovascular diseases such as arteriosclerosis and atherosclerosis. These diseases, if allowed to progress, can result in heart damage, heart failure or stroke. Arteriosclerosis of the extremities is a disease of the blood vessels characterized by narrowing and hardening of the arteries that supply the legs and feet. This causes a decrease in blood flow that can injure nerves and other tissues.

Heart disease is now the leading cause of death in the United States, Canada, Australia, New Zealand, and most European countries. Cancer is second, followed by stroke (cerebrovascular diseases), according to the National Center for Health Statistics of the Center for Disease Control and Prevention.

Atherosclerosis, more commonly known as hardening of the arteries, is a disease that affects arterial blood vessels, and is associated with heart disease. Cardiovascular disease is really a chronic inflammatory response that occurs in the walls of arteries.

This disease is particularly insidious because it normally begins in adolescence, is asymptomatic, and is not easily detected by diagnostic methods. In fact, it is often discovered only when serious symptoms emerge. In most cases, circulation of blood to the brain or heart is severely compromised. When this process occurs, it can cause a stroke or heart attack. Studies have found that for about 47% of women and 65% of men, the first symptom of atherosclerotic disease is either a heart attack or a condition referred to as "sudden death syndrome." By that term, we mean that sudden cardiac death occurs within an hour of the onset of symptoms. Maintaining a high level of antioxidant intake in the diet over one's lifespan might reduce the rate at which atherosclerotic disease can progress. That is what experimental evidence in animals is showing us.

The recognition of the importance of antioxidants and polyphenols became more pronounced a number of years ago, when researchers studied the phenomenon known as "the French Paradox." French people have a diet that is relatively high in fat in comparison to the diet found in other European countries. However, the French have a greatly decreased incidence of heart disease, relative to other countries.

This difference was attributed to the higher daily consumption of wines, which contained compounds that have a strong antioxidant effect. The average polyphenol content of white grapes is approximately 4,000 milligrams per kilogram. Yet when we analyzed the polyphenolic content of açai we found certain flavonoids known for their antioxidant capacity had five times the antioxidant activity of any other fruit or berry. Why is still a mystery, but it certainly caught the attention of lead scientists at the USDA who had not seen such activity in any other fruit with the same compounds.

Cancer research involving the effects of anthocyanins has also been promising. Numerous laboratories have reported that anthocyanins inhibit the promotion and progression of tumor cells *in vitro*.

According to research presented at a 2007 conference on antioxidants and berries, scientists now believe that these antioxidants work by:

1) Inhibiting the growth of pre-malignant cells.

2) Increasing the rate at which cells turn over, resulting in the cancer cells dying more quickly. This process is referred to as apoptosis.

3) Slowing down the growth of blood vessels that feed tumors. This phenomenon is called anti-angiogenesis.

4) Limiting the production of inflammatory compounds, called inflammatory mediators, which can initiate the appearance of tumors.

5) Reducing the level of damage to DNA.

In 2007, a very important study from the University of Pittsburgh discovered that anthocyanins are able to kill human cancer cells without affecting healthy cells *in vitro*.

In the course of their research, scientists determined the mechanism by which this occurs.

When cancer cells were exposed to the anthocyanin, cyanidin-3-rutinoside (C-3-R), abnormal cells respond by releasing peroxides that then selectively kill the cancer cell. However, when healthy cells are exposed to C-3-R, they do not release peroxides. This research is important because we identified in the açai berry the anthocyanin, C-3-R, as one of the two most predominant anthocyanins.

Another promising discovery was made in 2004 by Michigan State University. Researchers reported that anthocyanins could boost insulin production by up to 50%. More research is needed to see how clinically relevant this discovery is, but the very suggestion that anthocyanins might increase insulin is encouraging.

We hear physicians say constantly that people should reduce LDL-cholesterol and raise HDL cholesterol. Unless the amount of LDL-cholesterol is reduced, it can lead to inflammation along the lining of the arteries, and ultimately to a catastrophic blockage of an artery.

A marker of chronic inflammation in the blood is a substance called C-reactive protein (CRP). Both the American Heart Association and the US Centers for Disease Control and Prevention consider CRP a marker for the detection of cardiovascular disease.

In a study conducted in Italy reported in 2005, University of Parma scientists found that the total antioxidant capacity of the diet is inversely and independently related to the concentration of CRP. They felt this might be one of the explanations for the protective effect of antioxidant rich foods against cardiovascular disease (CVD). They also saw data suggesting that such foods might be of particular value to individuals who have high blood pressure, as individuals with hypertension seemed especially protected against CVD if they were consuming an antioxidant-rich diet.

Three years later this same group of scientists found that a diet rich in antioxidant capacity can reduce low-grade inflammation commonly found associated with type 2 diabetes and cardiovascular disease. The authors felt that selecting foods according to their high dietary total antioxidant capacity was important in reducing systemic inflammation.

Polyphenols have been shown *in vivo* (in the body) to decrease the harmful LDL-cholesterol levels that contribute to the build-up of plaque in arteries. Moreover, several studies have found both an increased antioxidant capacity of human blood plasma following ingestion of polyphenolic flavonoids, and a decrease in the harmful rate of LDL-cholesterol oxidation.

Based on the information you just read, you can now understand why scientists are willing to make statements such as, *"Consumption of fruit and vegetables is associated with a decreased risk of heart disease and cancer."* This makes even more sense given that there are nearly 600 different anthocyanins in the plant kingdom, many of which are colorful edible foods. But very few people are eating enough fruit and vegetables to benefit from all we know about the value of these foods.

As we have seen in this chapter, açai berries contain an array of powerful protective antioxidant substances. To understand how they work, it is important to understand their chemistry.

Chapter 9

The Nature of Antioxidants

What do you think would happen if you left a piece of red meat out on your kitchen counter for a few weeks? Not a very pleasant thought, is it? As you probably know, when meat is not frozen or refrigerated, but is left at a temperature range of between 40 to 140 degrees F (4.4 to 60 degrees C), bacteria of all sorts can thrive.

In fact, within this temperature danger zone, bacteria can double every 20 minutes! Two types of bacteria can thrive under these conditions - pathogenic bacteria that can make us sick, and spoilage bacteria that will make food rotten.

Long before we had modern refrigeration, humans learned how to preserve meat. North American Native Americans, who had access to blueberries, an antioxidant-rich food, employed one of the most interesting and successful preservation methods. These berries, rich in antioxidants, were applied directly to the surface of meat while it was drying. Then berries were mixed together with the meat, to form meat cakes.

The tribe could carry these cakes as it migrated, as could individuals who were traveling for days or weeks away from the family settlements. By combining blueberries with animal meat, the Natives learned that they could preserve the meat with antioxidants, so that it would be safe to eat for up to two years!

When we eat fruits or vegetables, we ingest a complex mixture of phenolic compounds. Epidemiological evidence suggests that maximum antioxidant benefit results from the balance and concentration of polyphenols and other antioxidants that are derived from a spectrum of antioxidant-rich foods.

Antioxidants are also known as reducing agents. A number of studies have established a relationship between the structure of different flavonoids and their relative effectiveness as reducing agents. So it is important to understand what is really going on when antioxidants do their job.

"Hydroxylation" is any chemical process that adds one or more hydroxyl groups (-OH) onto a compound (or radical), thereby oxidizing it. In biochemistry, hydroxylation reactions are often facilitated by enzymes called hydroxylases.

Recall from our earlier discussion that a free radical is really a structure that contains an unpaired electron. Reducing agents can donate an electron to a free radical, thereby stabilizing and inactivating the damaging radical. This process is called "neutralization."

During this process, the polyphenolic reducing agent, which can be a polyphenol from a food like açai, becomes an aroxyl radical, which is considerably more stable than the free radical that the polyphenol has reduced. When aroxyl radicals are created, the damaging oxidative chain reaction is stopped. But this process, repeated too often, diminishes the number of available hydrogen atoms. This relative lack of hydrogen can exhaust the hydroxylation that needs to continue.

Another factor that influences the antioxidant capacity of a flavonoid is the degree of hydroxylation on its so-called 'B' ring. This ability to increase antioxidant capacity with increasing degrees of hydroxylation is due to the presence of proanthocyanidins.

It is useful to know that these very same proanthocyanidins are present in the açai berry. Therefore, compounds in açai can act to replace needed hydrogen ions, which are necessary to continue and even increase this hydroxylation reaction. Açai contains the compounds that give it a very high degree of antioxidant ability, relative to many other foods.

How do food scientists know which foods provide us with the strongest antioxidants? In 1991, researchers with the US Department of Agriculture developed a test. This assay, known as the Oxygen Radical Absorbance Capacity (ORAC) assay, has been described as the single most important advancement in food chemistry developed by the USDA in over 125 years. For this reason, we sent samples of freeze-dried açai obtained in the Amazon to both the USDA and the world's most experienced contract laboratory that performs this assay.

The Oxygen Radical Absorbance Capacity (ORAC) Assay

The oxygen radical absorption capacity (ORAC) assay is one way of measuring the antioxidant capacity of a food. This analysis looks at how much a particular food inhibits free radical activity of certain free radicals. There are several different ORAC assays; each has been utilized to measure the ability of freeze-dried açai to scavenge free radicals.

Why is the ORAC assay used by so many scientists to compare the free radical capacity of so many foods?

Scientists working at the National Institutes of Aging, a division of the U.S. National Institutes of Health, developed the ORAC assay in 1991. In 1996, the lead scientist involved in its development joined the U.S. Department of Agriculture (USDA) Human Nutrition Research Center on Aging in Boston, and created a semi-automated, more efficient method to perform the ORAC assay. This created a more rapid system able to determine a food's antioxidant capacity.

The concept of ORAC is based on the hydrogen atom transfer reaction comparable to human biological processes. In the ORAC assay, Trolox, a water-soluble analogue of vitamin E, is used as a control standard - all results for any ingredient or food are compared against the antioxidant activity of this vitamin E analogue.

The peroxyl radical is the most abundant free radical produced in the body. The Trolox ORAC assay reveals how effectively an ingredient, compound, or food, quenches this particular free radical, compared to the ability of Trolox to act as an antioxidant.

Each ORAC assay result is expressed as an ORAC value in micromoles of Trolox equivalents (TE) per gram. Each unit of antioxidant capacity above one unit of Trolox suggests that the compared substance has stronger scavenging activity against free radicals. Foods that are the strongest antioxidants will have the highest ORAC values.

The USDA Agricultural Research Service (USDA/ARS) facility at the University of Arkansas has determined that there is a broad range of antioxidant activity in many foods Americans eat. ORAC scores vary from a low of 2 microgramsTE/gram for the tomato, up to 95 microgramsTE/gram for cranberries and wild blueberries.

This range was determined after the USDA/ARS performed hundreds of assays on many foods commonly consumed by Americans, which might have antioxidant activity. Their work even considered the possible changes in antioxidant activity of foods, which might occur during different seasons of the year, or from cultivated farm raised foods in different regions of the country.

Commercial laboratories occasionally report higher ORAC values for some foods, because the labs receive only one or two samples, instead of hundreds, from the submitter. Therefore, the USDA/ARS data is far more reliable, because it assayed numerous samples throughout the year taking into account variables such as when and where the food is harvested and their effect on antioxidant capacity.

By 2004, the USDA, led by Wu and colleagues, had compiled several long lists of the ORAC scores of a wide array of freeze-dried fruits, vegetables and nuts, published in the *Journal of Agricultural and Food Chemistry*. Our studies in collaboration with their laboratories showed that freeze-dried açai is 1,027 units greater than Trolox! The result is expressed as 1,027 micrograms of Trolox equivalents per gram. That result means that açai might have an extraordinary ability to neutralize the most dominant free radical produced in the human body, the peroxyl radical.

Açai's extraordinary antioxidant capacity against the peroxyl radical was a complete surprise. The result was more than 10 times higher than any other food reported by the USDA, when adjusted for moisture content, as almost all foods tested by USDA were also freeze-dried. It is worth keeping in mind that a few spices such as cloves, cinnamon, dried oregano leaf, and turmeric, have higher ORAC scores per gram than açai. Usually we add a pinch of a spice for flavor, while we eat a "serving size" of a food, usually 3-1/2 ounces (100 grams). Some spices can be extremely expensive compared to common foods when compared by weight, nor are spices consumed beyond their flavor contribution as a source of macro- and micro-nutrients (amino acids, vitamins, minerals, fiber, etc.). Yet because spices such as cinnamon have a high antioxidant ranking, there is every reason to have them in our diet.

There are also some foods with good antioxidant capacity before cooking, but which declines when cooked. For example, small red beans are a good source of fiber and various macro- and micro-nutrients. However, beans are not eaten raw or dried, instead they are cooked or fried. This dramatically decreases their antioxidant capacity. For this reason, we tested many samples of açai to see if the results were reliable, which took several years. Hence, we knew the power of açai as an antioxidant years before we published our results, but not before we were certain the results were believable. And we wanted to conduct many other studies involving other free radicals that effect human cells to see what açai would do to them.

In 2005, I co-authored a paper urging food scientists to avoid comparing antioxidant capacity between foods, because a food's antioxidant activity is just one marker of its overall nutritional and health benefit. For example, a botanical extract may have higher antioxidant capacity than freeze-dried açai, but that doesn't mean it has the same total health benefit of açai. That is because to produce an extract you have to remove something to increase the desired marker compound.

Take green tea for example. It contains compounds that are believed to have a positive impact on our health. However, recent studies have shown that the body can tell it's an extract and will not absorb the very compounds extracted to the degree it would if presented with plain green tea. The higher the level of the marker compounds the stranger it seems to the body compared to what it is familiar with. That's why we need to study the effect of botanical extracts on drug metabolism, especially since so many people are on prescription medications to avoid unwanted side effects.

It is also why we need to look at the historical use of a food, as discussed earlier for açai. With millions of people eating and drinking açai in Brazil, we would have some sign by now that people taking certain medications might have a problem with the palm berry. Yet there is no evidence that adverse drug-food interactions have occurred with açai in Brazil.

This is why I see no reason for introducing an açai extract, if the purpose is solely to increase the ORAC value per gram compared to the whole food. Again, if you concentrate something to make an extract, something has to go. This can upset the synergy between compounds that make the product not only beneficial to our health, but that make it safe to consume.

ORAC Scores Can Mislead

Understanding how to compare grams to ounces, as well as dry weight versus wet weight, is vitally important when comparing the ORAC units or that of any other assay reported for a food or food-based formulation (such as a dietary supplement).

While navigating the Internet, this claim was found touting chocolate's ORAC:

> *"Dark chocolate has more than 13,000 ORAC units and milk chocolate has about 6,700, according to the Chocolate Manufacturers Association."*

13,000 ORAC units! Wow!! That figure sounds pretty impressive, doesn't it? But is it, really? What exactly, does this impressive figure really mean? We can't determine the true significance of the number of "13,000 ORAC units" unless we know how many grams were required to provide this huge number of ORAC units.

To find out that answer, we can check directly with the Chocolate Manufacturers Association. According to the Association's website, dark chocolate has 13,120 ORAC units PER 100 GRAMS. When you divide 13,120 by 100, it turns out that dark chocolate's ORAC score is really 131.2 ORAC units per gram.

By making this simple calculation, we can now compare the ORAC scores of dark chocolate to the ORAC score of freeze dried açai on a gram per gram basis, for a typical chocolate serving size of 40 grams (approx. 1.4 ounces).

Once we know what the ORAC units are per gram we can produce a bar graph showing the difference between ORAC scores for freeze-dried açai, dark chocolate, and cocoa (used to make chocolate), as shown in Figure 5.

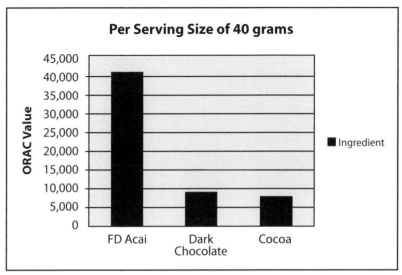

Figure 5

In the same way, we discovered that milk chocolate is 67.4 ORAC units per gram, depending on the amount of sugar, cocoa butter, stearic acid, etc., that it contains. An ORAC score of 67 certainly sounds less impressive than 6,700. Always look at the unit of measurement, and what weight (usually expressed in grams or ounces) an advertiser uses when referring to an ORAC score.

There is also the question of how many calories are in milk chocolate, whose ORAC scores range between 41 and 72 units per gram. Four ounces (a typical serving size), of a leading chocolate product has 560 calories. This amount is about equal to one quarter of an adult male's daily calorie requirements.

It also useful to know that 1-gram is equal to 0.03527 ounces; so 100 grams would be equivalent to approximately 3.5 ounces. With this information you can calculate true comparisons based on ORAC units or other assays whose results are reported as micrograms or grams.

But there is more to the chocolate story. *The Lancet*, the world's oldest medical journal, published an editorial on December 22, 2007, that revealed information chocolate lovers haven't been told.

In recent years chocolate has been touted as a source of antioxidants, especially dark chocolate. Consumers have been told that dark chocolate is a "health food." However, in its editorial, *The Lancet* charged dark chocolate promoters as being "deceptive." They point out that,

> *"When chocolate manufacturers make confectionary, the natural cocoa solids can be darkened and the flavonols, which are bitter,*

removed, so even dark-looking chocolate can have no flavanol. Consumers are also kept in the dark about the flavanol content of chocolate because manufacturers rarely label their products with this information."

The editorial went on to say:

"And, although flavanols, if they are present, seem to offer some health benefit, the devil in the dark chocolate is the fat, sugar, and calories it also contains. To gain any health benefit, those who eat a moderate amount of flavanol-rich dark chocolate will have to balance the calories by reducing their intake of other foods – a tricky job for even the most ardent calorie counter."

The point being made by *The Lancet* is that just because a food has a high antioxidant capacity, does not mean it is the best food to eat from a nutritional or health standpoint. Avoid being misled by often-meaningless ORAC scores taken out of context.

Consider another study about chocolate published in 2008 in the *American Journal of Clinical Nutrition*. In this study, over 1,000 women aged 70 to 85 participated. Women who ate chocolate daily were found to have an overall bone density 3.1 per cent lower than those who consumed it less than once a week. It is believed that even though chocolate contains calcium and flavonols, both linked to a positive effect on bone density, chocolates contain oxalate, an inhibitor of calcium absorption. In addition, most chocolates contain sugar (sucrose), which has been linked to calcium excretion.

Hence, having a chocolate as a treat occasionally may be fine; believing that it's a health food is another thing.

Comparison of Açai's Antioxidant Capacity with Pomegranates and Apples

Pomegranate

As just pointed out, chocolate might not be the healthiest of foods. But what about "superfoods" like pomegranates, touted for their antioxidant activity? How do these sources of antioxidants measure up to açai?

In searching the Internet, only one ORAC result for pomegranates appeared. However, the ORAC score did not reference a published study. As pointed out earlier, there is a lot of questionable information found on the Internet. The website claimed that the pomegranate powder they were promoting had an ORAC score of 105 micromoles.

The pomegranate powder was purchased and sent unopened to the lab in Boston with the most experience in performing ORAC assays. As can be seen in Figure 6, the actual ORAC score was 34 µmoleTE/g, about a third of the figure claimed on the Internet.

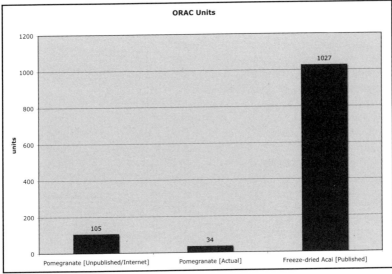

Figure 6

The pomegranate powder had about 1/30th of the antioxidant capacity of açai, when adjusted for moisture content. Solely relying on its lower ORAC score disregards research that have found properties of pomegranate that have been shown may have value in terms of human health.

This paucity of reliable scientific data on ORAC, beyond that reported by the USDA for 278 foods, leaves consumers vulnerable to unsupportable and exaggerated claims about exotic foods and their antioxidant capacity *in vitro* much less *in vivo*.

Blueberries

The health benefits of blueberries (*genus, Vaccinium*), are supported by a growing body of *in vitro* and *in vivo* studies published in the scientific literature. Interestingly, blueberries also contain some of the same anthocyanins found in açai. Lowbush and highbush blueberries contain some useful compounds, such as anthocyanins, proanthocyanidins, and flavonols, which vary according to the blueberry's exact genotype. Low bush (wild) blueberries (*V. angustifolium*) exceed the amount of these compounds compared to the highbush species. Numerous published studies have shown blueberries to contribute to neurological function, maintenance of healthy cholesterol, reduced risk of age-related loss of vision, and urinary tract health. Compounds in blueberries appear to give brain neurons protection from oxidative stress, as demonstrated in experiments performed with rodents and dogs. Research conducted at the USDA Agriculture Research Services (ARS) laboratory at Tufts University in Boston, led by James Joseph and colleagues, has shown that blueberry extracts demonstrate numerous health benefits in mice. This has encouraged widespread interest in the health benefits of blueberries.

Apples

Let us consider the apple, another nutritious fruit. After all, "an apple a day keeps the doctor away", doesn't it?

The antioxidant value of a small apple (with its peel), weighing about a quarter of a pound (113 grams), is equivalent to 1400 milligrams of Vitamin C. However, most of the antioxidant activity of an apple does not come from its vitamin C content, but rather from its combined phytochemical components. In fact, less than 0.4% of the apple's total antioxidant activity comes from vitamin C alone. Yet apples have been shown to inhibit colon cell proliferation *in vitro* by 43%.

Apples also decrease the incidence of mammary cancer and other tumors in rats. Studies performed on rats showed that if more apples are consumed, the inhibition is correspondingly greater. Just one apple inhibited 17% of tumors, but three apples inhibited 39%, while six apples a day inhibited tumor development by 44%.

Now, consider that an apple's Total ORAC score is between 22 to 43 micromoles Trolox equivalent per gram (μmoleTE/g), depending on the type of apple. Because an apple contains water, we have to adjust for it's moisture content, to fairly compare its antioxidant activity to other foods. By adjusting for moisture content açai pulp has an ORAC score of 630 μmoleTE/g, or 45 times the antioxidant capacity *in vitro* of a quarter pound apple.

So, given what we already know about the cancer inhibiting properties of a whole apple *in vitro* and in animals, we can only wonder about the cancer inhibiting properties of açai pulp. To date, only one study has been published on cancer cells and açai – that of a study by Pozo-Insfran and colleagues published in the *Journal of Agricultural and Food Chemistry* in 2006. The study did not use the whole fruit or its pulp. Instead it selected a fraction of compounds found in açai pulp and studied them in the laboratory (*in vitro*) using a leukemia cell line (HL-60). Depending on the concentration of the polyphenolic fractions tested, cell proliferation was reduced from 56% to 86%. This study was one of the first to demonstrate that flavonoids in açai contained compounds that were bioactive. The anti-proliferative effect on abnormal cells, resulting in the death (apotosis) of human leukemia cells, was important because it inspired further research. For example, in 2007-2008 Stoner and colleagues working at five universities in the United States looked at the effect of freeze-dried açai pulp in inhibiting tumors in rodents. These rodents were administered a cancer-causing chemical early in life known to cause esophageal tumors. This is the third most common cancer in the world. After being exposed to the carcinogen, açai pulp was added to their diet. At the end of the study there was a significant reduction in the number and size of tumors in these animals. Other antioxidant-rich foods, such as red raspberries, black raspberries, and blueberries also reduced the number of tumors found in the animals at end of life, but did not result in as small a size of tumors as was observed in the group of animals receiving açai pulp. Interestingly, noni (*Morinda citrifolia*) added to the diet showed no benefit. The study results were reported in June 2009 at an international symposium and awaiting publication in a journal.

Whether açai can prevent, mitigate or treat any cancer has yet to be demonstrated. Yet there is a significant body of scientific evidence emerging that suggests a number of compounds in açai might have anti-mutagenic and anti-carcinogenic properties. The bacterial reverse mutagenicity assay, commonly referred to as the "AMES Test", did not find açai to be mutagenic, nor have several other studies of an açai-based juice determined it was mutagenic, mitogenic, clastogenic, cytotoxic or toxic. The results of all these safety studies are being prepared for publication.

Measuring Inhibition of Oxidative Stress

Progress has also been made in the development of oxidative stress assays that have been useful in studying the attributes of açai. These assays allow one to have blood or urine checked for baseline antioxidant activity during oxidative stress.

Some examples of oxidative stress panels include: the plasma ORAC test; plasma thiobarbituric acid reactive substances (TBARS) test; urine total peroxides test; DNA damage markers test; cell-based antioxidant protection (CAP) assay; and the protein damage markers test. Numerous studies use these panels and others to measure the effect *in vitro* (out of the body) that eating antioxidant-rich foods might have in the human body (*in vivo*).

As we are learning, antioxidants from dietary sources interact with free radicals in the body and inhibit oxidative damage to cell membranes and DNA. These dietary antioxidants do not necessarily alter the antioxidant level in the body, but may decrease the level of oxidative stress.

That's an important point to understand. Oxidative stress levels are determined by the quantity of oxidized products of lipids, proteins and DNA. In general, the higher the ORAC value of an antioxidant-rich food, the more it should reduce the level of oxidative stress. That is a theory currently being tested by scientists in animals and humans.

This information is important because the etiology (cause or origin) of many of the major degenerative diseases, such as cancer, atherosclerosis, diabetes, etc., is associated with the reaction of free radicals with lipids, proteins and DNA. We hope and assume that the *in vitro* (out of the body) results correlate closely with the results in our bodies. In that case, antioxidant foods might prove to be as beneficial to humans as we would hope. Then comes the challenge of deciding which foods provide the best total package of nutrition and antioxidant capacity.

Further, it is recognized that the performance of an antioxidant compound may be influenced by numerous factors, such as lifestyle (e.g. alcohol intake, smoking, occupational toxins, etc.) and dietary factors. Also, the presence of chronic infections or diseases, all modified by the enzymatic and microbial environment of the particular individual's digestive system can modify the action of antioxidants.

Metabolites produced by bacteria in the gut are known to produce specific beneficial byproducts from the polyphenolic compounds and antioxidant vitamins found in açai. These metabolites may be as important, or even more important, than the parent compounds absorbed into our bodies via the small intestine. Future studies using metabonomic technology will help us learn what is going on in the gut, especially in terms of bacteria using açai and releasing metabolites that our body might require to support our health.

In other words, not only are the açai pulp's phytochemicals and nutrients absorbed into our blood stream through our gastrointestinal system but many of these compounds are further processed by bacteria in our large intestine. Then these new products are also absorbed into our bloodstream, as secondary metabolites of bacterial digestion.

Just in case you have been wondering what a "phytochemical" is, well it's a chemical naturally synthesized by plants. Phyto comes from the Latin *phyton* meaning plant or tree.

There is emerging evidence that these metabolites also serve as antioxidants *in vivo*. If this additional effect is proven to be true, then the goal is to supply our bodies with polyphenolic compounds and antioxidant vitamins on a regular basis, within the range of physiologic requirements needed by the body.

Once we achieve that goal, then we can let the body's digestive system and its bacterial hosts in the gut determine what is needed and when. This concept may also suggest that consumption of blends of different fruit juices with the açai berry could impart unique functional abilities

Other Antioxidant Assays of Açai – More Impressive Results

Free radicals, through the oxidative stress that they cause, are important causative factors in the development of diseases, and the acceleration of aging in general. This relationship has stimulated considerable interest in assessing the antioxidant capacity of foods and botanicals, and other nutritional antioxidant supplements.

As you now know, phenolics or polyphenolics are responsible for most of the antioxidant capacity in fruits and vegetables. Still, little is known about the absorption and metabolism of these particular components. We do know that improvement in the *in vivo* (in the body) antioxidant status in humans following consumption of antioxidant foods can have a profound effect on health over a life time, especially as we age.

We have already reviewed açai's ability to show superior free radical scavenging activity against the peroxyl radical and superoxide, compared to any other food.

The ORAC procedure that we discussed earlier uses 2,2-azobis (2-amidinopropane) dihydrochloride as a peroxyl radical source. This test is claimed to be relevant to biological systems because the peroxyl radical is the most abundant free radical found in the body. The ORAC method provides a basis from which to establish appropriate dietary intakes of foods containing antioxidants that might impact health outcomes. Whether they do requires experimental evidence *in vivo*.

The use of the oxygen radical absorbance capacity (ORAC) assay as a tool for antioxidant assessment is now the most accepted way of assessing the free radical scavenging capacity of a food. The creators of the ORAC assay have watched as other scientists made a great deal of progress in the use of ORAC test to measure other free radicals found in the body.

However, other oxidant sources (e.g., the hydroxyl radical and divalent copper) can also be used to characterize the relative strength of antioxidants in botanicals. Recently, other assays have also been developed, to refine our understanding about the protective effects of various foods and ingredients against these other oxidant chemicals.

The most common radical oxygen species that our bodies produce are superoxide (O_2-), hydroxyl radical (OH), peroxyl radical (RO_2), nitric oxide (NO) and peroxynitrite (ONOO). These free radical species have also been associated with many degenerative and chronic diseases associated with aging.

Research teams working with the original ORAC test have created new assays to measure the activity of other potentially damaging free radicals. One such test measures the hydroxyl radical scavenging capacity; this assay is called the HORAC test.

Although short lived, hydroxyl radicals are the most damaging of radicals. They are formed by the interaction of copper or iron with hydrogen. This reaction partly explains why men and women look older as they age. The HORAC assay measures the hydroxyl radical absorbance capacity.

Iron is required as a component of the oxygen-carrying proteins (myoglobin and hemoglobin) in red blood cells that transport oxygen from the lungs to our tissues. Hence, iron, an essential trace element, is in constant contact with oxygen. Scientists now believe that iron intake from the diet should be limited to only the minimum level required to maintain health.

The peroxynitrite radical can damage protein, DNA and other cellular structures. So yet another assay has been developed, called the NORAC, to determine the peroxynitrite (PON) radical scavenging capacity.

Actually, our immune system cells can produce peroxynitrite as part of our natural cellular defense system. In other words, free radicals are not all bad, because they can help the immune system kill cancer cells, and also attack pathogens that enter our body.

PON forms when superoxide and nitric oxide react together, or when certain other compounds interact in the body. Unfortunately, some of these chemical reactions can escape control. When they do so, the free radicals created by these reactions can cause peroxynitrite-related damage to the body.

Both the HORAC and the NORAC assays have found that freeze-fried açai has antioxidant capacity against both the hydroxyl radical and peroxynitrite.

Superoxide Scavenging Capacity of Açai

It is estimated that one percent of all oxygen consumed by an adult is converted to the free radical superoxide anion. This superoxide anion is believed to be the source of other reactive oxygen species such as hydrogen peroxide, peroxynitrite, and hydroxyl radicals (from hydrogen peroxide).

Therefore, the superoxide scavenging capacity in the human body is the first line of defense against oxidative stress. Scientists have stated that the, *"superoxide scavenging capacity in blood is considered very important in maintaining proper antioxidant status."*

An assay to measure superoxide antioxidant capacity has been developed, called the SORAC. Freeze-dried açai fruit was therefore subjected to this superoxide scavenging activity assay.

In 2006, we reported that: "freeze-dried Açai fruit pulp/skin powder has been shown to be extremely powerful in its antioxidant properties against superoxide (O_2-) by the super oxide assay." Previously, sprouted wheat had been the most studied source of superoxide scavenging activity in the diet. This food ranged from 160 to 450 unit equivalents per gram on the SORAC assay.

To our surprise, açai tested at 1,614 unit equivalents per gram. This extremely high result is more than four to five times greater than any other food the laboratory had ever tested. See the bar chart in Figure 7 to compare the superoxide scavenging activity of açai to the next highest food, wheat grass.

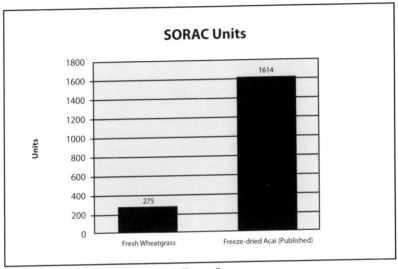

Figure 7

Açai has by far the highest superoxide neutralization ability of any fruit or vegetable yet tested.

This extraordinary finding is equally as important as açai's remarkably high ORAC value compared to other foods. The consumption of freeze-dried açai fruit could possibly reduce the production of other free radicals, owing to its remarkable superoxide scavenging activity.

By using all of these different ORAC assays, we discovered that açai scavenges the peroxyl, hydroxyl, peroxynitrite and superoxide radicals.

Yet there are still other free radical scavenging capacity assays that have been performed on freeze-dried açai, including the TEAC and FRAP assays.

TEAC Assay

The TEAC assay is shorthand for the Trolox equivalent antioxidant capacity assay; widely used as an *in vitro* assay to determine antioxidant activity of foods.

This assay utilizes the peroxidase activity of metmyoglobin on 2,2'-azinobis-(3-ethylbenzotiazoline-6-sulphonic acid) (ABTS), in the presence of hydrogen peroxide. This oxidation process forms the long-lived radical cation called ABTS. In the presence of antioxidant reductants and hydrogen donors, the absorbance of ABTS is quenched in proportion to the food's antioxidant capacity.

The TEAC assay uses a water-soluble vitamin E analogue, just as the ORAC assay does, to standardize results and measure the rate at which oxidation is inhibited. Some antioxidants can delay the formation of ABTS, while others quench the free radical cation; some are able to do both.

The assay does have some limitations, because it can be used only for hydrophilic (water-soluble) antioxidants. This limitation explains why the TEAC assay is often used to analyze beverages and other fluids for their antioxidant capacity.

Blueberries have been tested via the TEAC assay, and were found to have a value of 39.45 micromoles Trolox equivalent per gram (μmoleTE/g). Pomegranate (*Punica granatum*), another fruit touted for its antioxidant capacity, has been reported to be 4.59 μmoleTE/g. The TEAC values for rambutan (*Nephelium lappaceum*), mangosteen (*Garcinia mangostana*), dragon fruit (Hylocereus undatus), and passion fruit (*Passiflora foetida*), are below that of pomegranate, at 3.07, 3.00, 0.69, and 0.59 μmoleTE/g, respectively.

I decided to perform the TEAC on açai. The lowest score that came back from the laboratory for a freeze-dried açai sample was 744 μmoleTE/g.

As can be seen in Figure 8, the result of the TEAC assay shows that açai is almost 20 times higher than blueberries based on the TEAC assay, and many times greater than that for all of the other fruits for which TEAC scores have been reported.

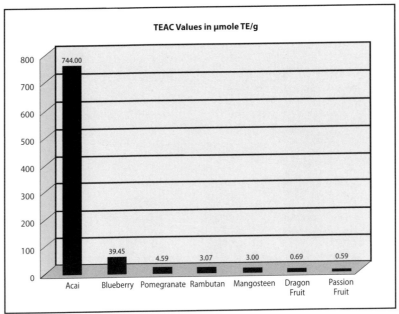

Figure 8

Other foods rich in antioxidants, such as black currants, cranberries, boysenberries *(Rubus deliciosus)*, blackberries *(Rubus fruticosus)*, and strawberries, all have inferior TEAC assay scores, when compared to açai.

FRAP Assay

The ferric reducing antioxidant power (FRAP) assay looks at the antioxidant potential of both foods and biological fluid. For researchers interested in oxidative stress and its effects, the FRAP is another assay similar to the ORAC and TEAC assays. But some scientists contend that the FRAP assay is superior to either the ORAC or TEAC assays, in terms of determining a food's antioxidant capacity.

According to a study published in *Current Opinions in Lipidology* in 2006, blueberries were at the top of the list of fruits based on the FRAP assay, with an antioxidant content of 8.2 µmoleTE/g per 100 grams (the usual "serving size") or 82 micromoles per gram. Blackberries were second, at 51 µmoleTE/g, although another paper reported it to be 77 µmoleTE/g. The juice with the highest antioxidant content was grape juice, which had 16 µmoleTE/g. To find out the FRAP score for açai, we had a FRAP assay performed on freeze-dried açai.

As shown in Figure 9, açai's FRAP assay resulted in a score of 249 µmoleTE/g, or 24.9 µmoleTE/g per 100 grams. This result suggests that açai may have at least three times the antioxidant capacity of either blueberries or blackberries.

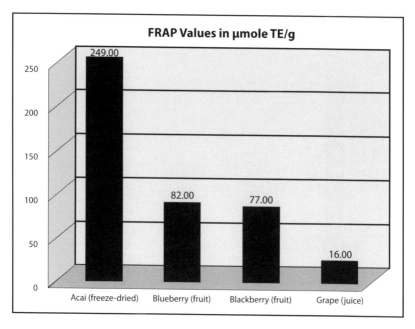

Figure 9

Claims of Antioxidant Capacity for Various "Superfoods"

Many individuals are curious about the antioxidant activity of exotic foods like noni (*Morinda citrifolia*), mangosteen (*Garcinia mangostana*), red aronia (*Aronia arbutifolia*), and wolfberries (*Lycium barbarum*).

The problem is that one cannot confirm many of the claims made about their antioxidant claims, as the results are not published in peer review journals. Then why are these foods referred to as "superfoods"?

Some websites substantiate their claim by mentioning the name of the lab where they did the study. However, that is not adequate proof without knowing what was tested, when, using what methods, and whether for one sample or many. The lab could even have received a sample that had been doctored with antioxidants, such as vitamin C or botanical extracts, to raise the level of antioxidant activity.

There is a lot of misrepresentation of the antioxidant capacities of foods found on the Internet. For example, in 2007, an ingredient supplier promoted a Patagonian berry, the maqui berry (*Aristotelia chilensis*) as being far superior to açai in terms of its antioxidant capacity *in vitro*. To substantiate their claim the company reported that açai has an ORAC of only 300 units. After sending them a copy of our research, done in collaboration with the USDA, and published in a leading journal in applied chemistry, even found on Google, they refused to acknowledge their error. Then someone told me that their product was not pure maqui but a formulation containing ingredients that could increase the ORAC score. Whether this product is still available is of no concern, but it does illustrate that one has to be careful when comparing ORAC scores. Some papers I have read in recent years even mention that the ORAC scores are based on a "modified method" and then provide insufficient information to understand how it is different from the validated method that is used by food scientists with years of experience testing foods using the published assay method.

This is not to say that the maqui berry may not be a good antioxidant, as a paper published in 2002 did show it had antioxidant attributes *in vitro*.

Another problem that can develop is when the supplier of a "superfood" fruit or berry is in short supply. For example, in 2008, a pomegranate juice filed a lawsuit against another company because its independent testing in numerous labs revealed that the juice of the defendant, "consists primarily of cane sugar and corn sweetener, and contains little pomegranate solids", this despite the company's claim on their label that the product contained "NO added sugar or sweeteners." The US District Court in Los Angeles agreed with the plaintiff and ruled against the defendant. The court noted that even after the problem was reported to the defendant, it did not replace or recall the mislabeled juice from the marketplace. This can happen when the supply chain for a food has difficulty meeting rising demand. But in this case the mislabeling seemed intentional and may have to some degree been due to a shortage of pomegranate from suppliers.

This example highlights what happens in the world of commerce, and the kind of information that might be found on the Internet. For this reason, I have not relied on the internet for information, or information provided by companies touting various "superfoods." Instead, as can be seen in the references to this book, published research in the scientific literature is preferred.

Chapter 10

Açai: The Highest Antioxidant Capacity of Any Fruit or Vegetable?

Free radicals are reactive unpaired electrons (called oxidants) that can have acute or chronic adverse effects on normal physiological function. This negative effect is referred to as oxidative stress.

The main role of antioxidants is to interact with excessive free radical activity, and mop up or quench these free radicals so they are rendered harmless.

In a previous chapter, we discussed the fact that the USDA has used the ORAC assay to test almost all of the fruits and vegetables consumed in the United States to determine their antioxidant activity. The USDA reported that wild blueberries and cranberries had the highest average ORAC value of any food tested. Cranberries had the highest score, a total (hydrophilic and lipophilic) ORAC of 95.

You can imagine my surprise, when we tested freeze-dried açai fruit pulp, and the Total ORAC value was determined to be 1,027, over ten times higher than the highest ORAC scores for any food at the time! Thinking at first this may be due to some kind of laboratory error, samples were sent to USDA for confirmation. Since almost all of the foods USDA tested were first freeze-dried before being assayed, the possibility that the extraordinary difference between the results for açai and cranberries or blueberries wasn't due to differences in moisture content. To insure that the result obtained was reliable, numerous samples were tested for several years. Again and again the pulp had the highest antioxidant activity of any food in the American diet. FRAP and TEAC assays provided further confirmation, as discussed in chapter 9.

Its peroxyl scavenging capacity and remarkable superoxide scavenging capacity made açai take its place among other well-known antioxidants. We did examine spray-dried açai samples; unfortunately, the assays revealed that spray drying reduced the pulp's antioxidant capacity.

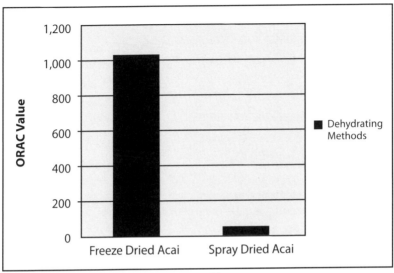

Figure 10

Figure 10 shows the difference in ORAC capacity between freeze-dried açai and spray-dried açai.

Why would freeze-drying prove to be such a superior drying method, in terms of the antioxidant capacity?

Walter S. Pebley, a professional engineer and authority on freeze-drying, and James S. Baglien, a physiologist, provide the following explanation:

> *Freeze-drying is a process in which water is removed as vapor directly from ice, without passing through the liquid state. This process is called sublimation, and requires reduced atmospheric pressure to occur. All other drying methods use evaporation; that is, water is removed as vapor from liquid water with heated air.*
>
> *Freeze-dried açai pulp does not require heat during the sublimation process. Through freeze-drying açai pulp retains its original characteristics of color, taste, and nutrient and phytochemical content. In addition, the freeze-dried pulp retains at least 95% of the phytochemicals and nutrients found in the fruit at the time the seed is extracted and the pulp is frozen.*

Freezing slows or stops most enzymatic chemical reactions. This effect is especially important when dealing with a tropical fruit that, once removed from its parent host, is programmed to decay rapidly.

Second, the freeze-drying process occurs under a vacuum in the absence of oxygen. This vacuum prevents oxidative reactions from occurring. Third, freeze-drying can be performed at very low temperatures - lower than other drying methods. At these low temperatures, enzymatic and bacterial breakdown cannot occur. Further, chemical changes that might occur are minimized.

Other benefits of freeze-drying are: (i) the fruit reconstitutes to its original state when placed in water; (ii) it remains stable at room temperature; (iii) the weight of the product is reduced by 70 to 90 percent; and (iv) because it is light in weight, it lowers handling and shipping costs. An added benefit comes from the low water content of freeze-dried açai pulp – it virtually eliminates microbiological problems or rancidity concerns (based on shelf-life studies).

The National Aeronautics and Space Administration (NASA) understood the advantages of freeze-drying years ago. Astronauts in space, with no fresh food to consume, can survive for months by eating a diet of freeze-dried foods. According to data published in 2004 and 2005 by the USDA in the *Journal of Agricultural and Food Chemistry*, one can compare açai's Total ORAC value to common fruits and vegetables on a gram for gram basis, as shown in Tables 2 and 3. By 2007, the USDA had analyzed 278 common plant foods for antioxidant capacity using ORAC, including açai.

Table 2.

Comparison of ORAC Capacity of Açai and other Fresh Fruit

Fresh or Raw Fruit	Total ORAC (micromoles TE/g)	Fresh or Raw Fruit	Total ORAC (micromoles TE/g)
Açai fruit (freeze-dried)	1,027	Apple, Golden Delicious (no peel)	22
Açai fruit (fresh)*	185	Applesauce	20
Cranberry	95	Avocado (Haas)	19
Blueberry (low bush)	93	Pears (green cultivars)	19
Plums (black)	73	Pear (Red Anjou)	18
Plums	62	Orange (Navel)	18
Blueberry (cultivated)	62	Peaches	18
Blackberry	53	Tangerines	16
Raspberry	49	Grapefruit (red)	16
Apple, Red Delicious (with peel)	43	Apricot	13
Açai fruit, frozen	40*	Grapes (red)	13
Apple, Granny Smith	39	Grapes (green)	11
Strawberry	36	Mango	10
Cherries (sweet)	34	Kiwifruit	9
Apple, Red Delicious (no peel)	29	Bananas	9
Apple, Gala	28	Pineapples	8
Apple, Golden Delicious (with peel)	27	Nectarines	8
Apple, Fuji	26	Peaches, canned in heavy syrup	4
		Cantaloupe	3
		Honeydew melons	2
		Watermelon	1

*Laboratory analysis of hydrophilic ORAC value only (Brunswick Labs, 2005), Schauss, AG et al. *Federation of Societies Experimental Biology Journal*, 2006c.)

(Source: Wu, X et al. *Journal of Food Composition and Analysis*, 2004; Wu, X et al. *Journal of Agricultural and Food Chemistry*, 2004; Schauss AG et al. *Journal of Agricultural and Food Chemistry*, 2006a; Schauss AG et al. *Journal of Agricultural and Food Chemistry*, 2006b; Schauss, AG et al. *Federation of Societies Experimental Biology Journal*, 2006.)

Table 3.
Comparison of ORAC Capacity of Açai and Fresh, Raw and/or Cooked Vegetables

Fresh, Raw or Cooked Vegetables	Total ORAC (micromoles TE/g)	Fresh, Raw or Cooked Vegetables	Total ORAC (micromoles TE/g)
Açai fruit (Freeze-dried)	1,027	Salsa	10
Açai fruit (fresh)	185	Peppers, red sweet	9
Açai (spray-dried)	55-155	Romaine lettuce	9
Artichoke	94	Sweet potato, cooked	8
Peas (black eye)	43	Cauliflower	6
Butterhead lettuce	33	Celery	6
Cabbage (red)	31	Green Peas, frozen	6
Broccoli (raab)	30	Ketchup	6
Asparagus	30	Peppers, Green Sweet (Bell Peppers)	6
Beets	28	Iceberg Lettuce	6
Spinach	26	Tomato Juice	6
Eggplant	25	V8 Vegetable Juice	6
Broccoli	16	Corn, frozen	5
Potato, Russet, cooked	16	Pumpkin, raw	5
Potato, red, cooked	13	Corn, canned	4
Carrot	12	Green Peas, canned	4
Green leaf lettuce	12	Snap Beans, canned or raw	3
Red lead lettuce	12	Tomato, raw	3
Onions, yellow and red	11	Lima Beans, canned	2
Potato, white, cooked	11	Cucumber, with and without peel	1
Radishes	10		

(Source: Wu, X et al. *Journal of Food Composition and Analysis*, 2004; Wu, X et al. *Journal of Agricultural and Food Chemistry*, 2004; Schauss AG et al. *Journal of Agricultural and Food Chemistry*, 2006a; Schauss AG et al. *Journal of Agricultural and Food Chemistry*, 2006b; Schauss, AG et al. *Federation of Societies Experimental Biology Journal*, 2006.)

Tables 2 and 3 are not really fair comparisons between freeze-dried açai fruit and other common fruits and vegetables, because there is a significant difference in the water content between fresh fruit and dried fruit.

A more accurate comparison needs to adjust for the moisture content of each food sample assayed. Brunswick Laboratories (Wareham, MA), an ORAC assay lab that has validated its method, provided the data for common foods and freeze-dried açai. These results have been adjusted for moisture content on a gram-to-gram basis, by having approximately the same amount of water in each food.

As shown in the tables, fresh açai fruit had a total ORAC score of 185, compared to the 1,027 ORAC score for freeze-dried pulp.

Why the huge difference? The fresh sample was harvested in the Amazon, then rushed to the airport and flown directly to the USA, from the Amazon to Miami and then onto Boston in a container filled with dry ice. Once it arrived in Boston it was immediately taken to laboratory and assayed. This experience illustrates just how quickly the antioxidant capacity of açai declines after harvesting.

Researchers logically assumed that because of the high ORAC score was the pulp would contain much higher concentrations of compounds associated with antioxidant activity. But to everyone's surprise, freeze-dried açai turned out to have much lower levels of these compounds than are found in blueberries, or in other berries with elevated ORAC values.

To make matters even more puzzling, we published the following information: the total phenolics in açai were found to be only 13.9 mg/g Gallic Acid Equivalents (GAE). In a recent paper, the ratio between hydrophilic ORAC and total phenolics was found to vary dramatically, from less than two to more than 100, for different groups of foods. For most fruits and vegetables, this ratio is about 10. However, the ratio found for the pulp was 50, five times greater than the ratio found in any other fruit. This unusual ratio raised questions about whether açai contained stronger antioxidants compounds than found in other berries on an equal weight basis.

Work is continuing to determine why açai has antioxidants that seem to be more powerful than those of other fruits and berries.

Why Does Açai Have Greater Antioxidant Capacity?

Plants use antioxidants to cope with oxidative stress. So, what kind of powerful stressors does an açai palm endure, to give it such an unusually high antioxidant capacity?

Açai palms form the canopy of the flood plains in the eastern Amazon basin north and south of the Equator. The only time this palm needs shade is during its juvenile stage. Once the açai palm becomes more developed and bears fruit, it can withstand intense UV radiation emitted by the sun.

The development of extraordinary antioxidant capacity is particularly seen in the lowlands, near rivers and their tributaries, and along Brazil's coastal swamps, although the difficulty of obtaining samples and freeze-drying them quickly after harvesting leaves an absence of data that fruit from higher.

Prolonged seasonal flooding predictably occurs in flood plains. Normally, if one puts a tropical food crop like corn under water for more than a few days, it will die due to anoxia, a lack of oxygen. Anoxia can easily kill a plant when it happens for even a short time. However, unlike most plants that cannot survive in a state of anoxia for very long, the açai palm can withstand weeks, even months under such stress. Its survival is possible because oxygen diffusion takes place from its leaves into the roots.

The açai palm has also developed the ability to synthesize energy in the form of adenosine triphosphate (ATP) in its cells, even in the absence of oxygen. In the açai palm tree's root system, aerobic respiration can occur at the same time that anaerobic metabolism occurs. Rice (another monocot type of plant) can do this too. That characteristic explains why rice does so well submerged in paddies filled with water.

Thus, the açai palm is not just an ordinary palm, but is one that has evolved over time to cope with all kinds of severe climatic and environmental stresses. Such resilient adaptation is not surprising, when one considers that it rains almost every day in the Amazon. Closer to the Atlantic Ocean, another phenomena occurs that may be unique in the world. When the tide rises in the ocean, it forces back the discharge of water pouring out of the Amazon River. This results in water levels in the river rising and thousands of square miles of açai palms being submersed. As the tide goes down, so does the water level in and near the river. This cycle occurs twice a day, every day.

How each stressor directly causes an increase in the production of antioxidant compounds is a mystery. For example, an eggplant, which also has a very dark skin full of anthocyanins, shows very low antioxidant absorbance capacity, as seen by its low ORAC score. But the fruit of the açai palm, which has a similarly dark skin and comparable anthocyanins, has an extraordinarily high antioxidant absorbance capacity, with a correspondingly huge ORAC score.

Antioxidants in Açai

What antioxidant compounds are contained in the açai palm fruit? Over the last few years we have been continuing to characterize and isolate pure compounds for research. Using highly sophisticated analytical methods it has been determined that açai pulp contains a number of anthocyanins, including two predominant anthocyanins, cyanidin-3-glucoside and cyanidin-3-glucoside-coumaraterutinoside.

Other phenolic compounds that are often found in foods touted for their health promoting properties are also found in açai, including quercetin, protocatechic acid, catechin and epicatechin. It is noteworthy that these compounds are found in green tea, chocolate, grapes, many antioxidant-rich berries, and apples.

Other compounds found in açai include: eriodictyol-7-glucoside; luteolin-4-glucoside; isoquercitin and quercitin-3-arabinoside; eriodictyol (found in citrus fruits); luteolin, chrysoeriol, eupatorin, orientin, homoorientin, vitexin, isovitexin, dihydrokaempferol, and kaempferol (found in onions, scallions, kale, broccoli, apples, berries and tea).

Chapter 11

Benefits of Antioxidants

Scientists still aren't 100% certain, but almost every study of diet suggests that consuming five more or servings of fruits and vegetables a day has a significant benefit to our health.

A British study reported in 2007, involved 20,000 healthy men and women had followed their lifestyle for 15 years. Not surprisingly, quitting smoking had the most significant impact on life extension. But what was surprising was that eating five servings of fruit and vegetables each day was the second most important contributor to a healthier and longer life. Moderate drinking of alcoholic beverages and moderate exercise followed fruits and vegetables. People who drink moderately, exercise, quit smoking and eat five servings of fruit and vegetables each day live on average 14 years longer than people who adopt none of these behaviors, according to the study.

Recent epidemiological studies and clinical trials have determined that there is an inverse correlation between the intake of antioxidant-rich fruits and vegetables and the prevalence or occurrence of diseases such as cardiovascular disease, diabetes, cancer, inflammatory diseases, and age-related diseases. Does açai have the attributes to contribute to disease prevention?

Oxidative Stress

Dietary antioxidants are nutrients that are effective in the prevention of oxidative stress-related diseases. Because açai fruit contains numerous proanthocyanidins it may even do more than just reduce the risk of diseases. Açai may also delay some external signs of aging. Oxidation causes the most visible sign of oxidative stress and aging on our skin. Hence, it makes good sense to maintain optimal antioxidant status. This conclusion may also explain why so many sunscreens now incorporate antioxidants into their formulations.

Oxidative stress can also be caused by peroxynitrite, the free radical known to damage the vascular endothelium. In the arterial wall that carries blood, the endothelium is the lining that comes in contact with the blood. Repeated nitrosative stress, similar to oxidative stress, caused by the peroxynitrite free radical, if not kept in check, can lead to atherosclerosis.

A study reported in 2009 by David Bell and colleagues at the Indiana University School of Medicine in Fort Wayne, found that açai pulp possesses vasoactive and vasoprotective capacity. It does this by protecting the arterial wall (the endothelium) from external attack by superoxide.

Inflammation

Inflammation is a natural response of the immune system to chemical, metabolic or physical assault, from a number of sources, including pathogenic organisms. In some chronic conditions, inflammation is associated with debilitating diseases.

One of the ways to reduce acute or chronic inflammation is to inhibit the activity of a compound called cyclooxygenase-2 (COX-2). Using a cyclooxygenase inhibitor assay, we found that açai pulp inhibited COX-2 activity. Although non-steroidal anti-inflammatory drugs (NSAIDs) or synthetic COX inhibitors are more powerful, recent studies have shown that COX-2 inhibitor drugs increase the risk of serious adverse events.

Lipid Peroxidation

During a trip to Brazil some years ago, it came to my attention that açai is associated with an ability to decrease cholesterol levels in individuals with moderately elevated cholesterol. Açai seemed to particularly help those individuals who need to improve their ratio of low-density to high-density lipoprotein-cholesterol (LDL-HDL cholesterol).

In 2006, we reported in the *Journal of Agricultural and Food Chemistry* that freeze-dried açai contains 82 percent of its fats as mono-unsaturated and poly-unsaturated fatty acids, those "good" fats lauded by nutritionists.

Americans in particular, along with a growing number of people around the world, consume too much saturated fat and/or hydrogenated fat in comparison to these good fats. This excess of saturated fat has been shown experimentally and epidemiologically to contribute to coronary vascular diseases. Hence, açai is a rich source of desirable fats that are good for the heart and the circulatory system.

Phytosterols are plant fats that are rather different in chemical structure to animal fat cholesterol. Some researchers believe that these fats may be effective in the treatment or prevention of elevated cholesterol, a condition known as hypercholesterolemia.

In 2006, in the same journal, we also reported that açai contains appreciable amounts of phytosterols, predominantly beta-sitosterol, campesterol, and sigmasterol. These compounds have been shown in numerous studies to have lipid-lowering properties.

It is my opinion that certain vitamins, minerals, fatty acids and phytosterols, acting in concert with antioxidant compounds, work together to provide a benefit in contributing to maintaining a healthy cholesterol ratio.

Stress

In 2005, the Universidade Federal do Rio Grande do Norte in Brazil reported that proteins in açai pulp have considerable inhibitory activity towards human salivary alpha-amylase. They also block trypsin. This action is called antitryptic activity.

Determining salivary alpha-amylase (sAA) levels in humans is useful in measuring the degree of stress an individual is experiencing. An increase in sAA correlates with an increase in norepinephrine (also called noradenaline), and mirrors changes in cortisol levels that correlate with stress. A higher sAA level means that the individual is experiencing greater amounts of stress.

Norepinephrine is produced by the adrenal gland and released into the bloodstream as part of the fight-or-flight response. Both a hormone and a neurotransmitter, norepinephrine is also released by nerve endings of the sympathetic nervous system. Such release results in an increase in the heart rate, blood pressure, and blood sugar level.

Hence, the proteins in açai may contribute to peoples' ability to cope with everyday stress. This fact may explain why native Brazilians who regularly drink açai notice a difference within days of stopping their consumption of this beverage, as noted by a National Academy of Sciences survey conducted in Brazil in the late 1980's, and discussed previously.

Fast and Slow Antioxidant Properties

An antioxidant assay developed at the University of California at Irvine, School of Medicine, called the Total Anti-oxidant (TAO) assay, can determine a food's antioxidant capacity.

The TAO is able to differentiate antioxidants into two types. It analyzes a "slow-acting" component, which includes complex organic antioxidants (e.g. phenolics), and a "fast-acting" (or vitamin C type) component. The association of the fast-acting type with vitamin C reflects the knowledge that vitamin C loses its antioxidant activity much faster than other antioxidant sources do, because vitamin C is more quickly excreted out of the body.

After performing the TAO assay on samples of freeze-dried açai sent to the lab, they discovered that the pulp was both "slow-acting" as well as a "fast-acting." This property was the first ever reported for any food. The results of this study were included in our 2006 paper published in the *Journal of Agricultural and Food Chemistry*.

Protection of Human White Blood Cells

A neutrophil is a type of white blood cell that is involved in killing and digesting microorganisms it has engulfed by a process called phagocytosis. The principal phagocytes include the neurtophils and another type of white blood cell called a monocyte. These two work together to engulf bacteria and other microorganisms, aged red blood cells, and foreign matter that have entered the body. Neutrophils constitute one type of white blood cell, while granulocytes are a subgroup of neutrophils. Granulocytes contain tiny sacs of enzymes that play a major role in the body's defense against fungi, bacteria and viruses. The sacs of enzymes in the granulocytes help the cell effectively kill and digest pathogens via phagocytosis.

If a person has too many neutrophils, a condition called neutrophilia, it is usually an indication that the person has developed an acute bacterial infection. If someone has a decreased percentage of neutrophils in their blood, called neutropenia, it might indicate that the person has a viral infection, or is experiencing the side effects of chemotherapy or radiotherapy during cancer therapy.

Neutropenia lowers the ability of white blood cells to conquer fungal and/or bacterial infections. For these reasons, a study of the effect of the açai pulp on neutrophil cells was of interest. We wanted to see how these components of the immune system would respond if açai pulp was added while subjecting fresh human cells to conditions that create oxidative stress. Such conditions mimic the state that many believe is linked to a wide range of diseases.

As reported in 2006 in the *Journal of Agricultural and Food Chemistry*, a study was performed as follows. Blood samples were provided by healthy volunteers. As expected their cells contained an amount of neutrophils within the normal range found in healthy individuals. 100% of the neutrophil cells were harvested and used to evaluate their response once reactive oxygen species (ROS) appeared. Next, neutrophils were treated with açai pulp at various dilutions, or left untreated to serve as a control. Both groups of neutrophils were exposed to hydrogen peroxide for 45 minutes. This test tube situation is similar to processes that occur in the human body, resulting in oxidative stress from the body's release of hydrogen peroxide and the resulting production of ROS. This bioassay is commonly used to estimate the effectiveness of any given agent of interest in terms of how efficiently it is able to quench hydrogen peroxide molecules and thereby stop the production of harmful and damaging ROS.

The results of each study consistently showed that pre-treatment of fresh human neutrophil cells with açai pulp resulted in a reduction in ROS production. The formation of ROS was significantly inhibited, even at extremely low doses of the pulp. Repeated experiments consistently showed that açai diluted of one part per trillion significantly inhibited ROS production. Not until it was diluted down again to one-tenth part per trillion did the antioxidant activity stop. The result of this experiment demonstrated that it was possible for açai pulp's antioxidants to work within the physiologic range that occurs in the human body. The study demonstrated that açai pulp has a substantial inhibitory effect on ROS formation in human neutrophil cells. The findings indicate that the active antioxidant compounds in the pulp were bioactive and able to enter human cells in a fully functional form and perform oxygen-quenching functions at extremely low doses.

This experiment may also explain why just a few ounces of an unfilitered/unclarified açai-based juice consumed daily (containing freeze-dried açai that has not lost its antioxidant activity, phytochemical composition, or nutritional value and which was used in this study) might mitigate oxidative stress-related conditions in the human body. However, many studies need to be conducted before we know for sure. The evidence from this study is tantalizing, and the jury is still out waiting to learn more before agreeing that it might benefit humans in myriad ways. When taken in its totality, the many studies performed and reported in the scientific literature to date suggest that in time the verdict will favor açai, especially when we unravel its mechanisms of action, and how it effects cellular signaling and influences gene expression.

Chapter 12
Summary and Conclusions

To summarize the preceding chapters of this book, the following list highlights major points made in this book.

1) Açai fruit has a long history of use as a food by natives living in the Amazon going back to prehistorical times.

2) In its lifetime, a typical açai palm can produce over 2,200 pounds (1,000 kilos) of açai fruit.

3) Up to 7,500 açai palm trees have been found growing in areas of the eastern Amazon River delta, in surveys conducted by the Brazilian government, suggesting a limitless supply of the fruit that can meet growing demand.

4) Açai is a staple source of nutrition, which when combined with manioc flour constitutes a major source of calories for people living in the flood plains of the Amazon River delta. In cities, many individuals consume up to 64 ounces (2 liters) of fresh açai pulp a day.

5) British, Portuguese, and American botanists have documented the historical harvesting and use of açai over a period of more than two centuries.

6) Açai pulp is mixed into numerous foods by natives living in the Amazon and consumed at almost every meal.

7) There are no significant adverse events associated with the consumption of açai pulp reported in the scientific literature.

8) All research concerning açai pulp has been published in peer reviewed scientific journals. The vast majority of studies have been performed using freeze-dried açai pulp.

9) Freeze-drying is a superior method to preserve the nutritional, phytochemical, and antioxidant capacity of açai, compared to spray drying, sun drying, or other methods of preservation.

10) Studies on the composition and bioactivities of açai pulp have been published in ranked peer-reviewed journals such as the *Journal of Agricultural and Food Chemistry*.

11) In our body, free radicals react with organic substrates such as proteins and lipids and can damage DNA in our cells. Oxidation of these biomolecules can cause damage, resulting in disruption of function that can accelerate aging and/or lead to disease.

12) The oxygen radical absorbance capacity (ORAC) assay is a reliable and validated method to compare the antioxidant capacity of a food to quench the peroxyl radical, the most dominant free radical produced in the human body. However, the assay is *in vitro* and any implications that a substance will result in reducing the formation of this reactive oxygen species requires *in vivo* evidence.

13) It has been suggested that units of ORAC should simply be called "anti-aging points."

14) The USDA has analyzed nearly 300 fruits, vegetables and nuts, all plant foods, commonly found in the American diet, and açai pulp, for their antioxidant capacity using the ORAC assay.

15) The Total ORAC of freeze-dried açai is the highest reported for any food, with the exception of a few spices, and reported in the scientific literature to be 1,027 micromoles of Trolox equivalent per gram (µmol TE/g).

16) Published studies on the antioxidant capacity of açai against the peroxyl radical rank it at the top of ORAC charts among fruits or vegetables – 102,700 total ORAC units per 100 grams. Cranberries and wild blueberries Total ORAC score has been reported to be in the range of 9,000 units by comparison. This does not mean that one food is superior to another just based on its ORAC score, as all fruits and vegetables make important contributions to the human diet including the provision of phytochemicals with demonstrated antioxidant capacity.

17) The hydrophilic ORAC capacity of freeze-dried açai, at an ORAC of 998 µmol TE/g, is the highest of any food.

18) The lipophilic ORAC capacity of freeze-dried açai, at an ORAC of 29 µmol TE/g, is the highest of any fruit or vegetable.

19) The Trolox equivalent antioxidant capacity (TEAC) assay of freeze-dried açai is 744 µmol TE/g, the highest of any food reported to date.

20) The ferric reducing antioxidant power (FRAP) assay of freeze-dried açai is 249 µmol TE/g, among the highest reported for any food to date.

21) An açai-based fruit juice, that does not clarify or filter freeze-dried or frozen açai, has been shown to inhibit lipid peroxidation of fats in the body based on the TBARS assay, of subjects who participated in a randomized, double-blind, placebo-controlled, cross-over study.

22) The superoxide anion radical scavenging capacity of freeze-dried açai is 1,614 SOD units, the highest of any food. The superoxide radical is implicated in the pathogenesis of numerous diseases. The radical also produced the highly toxic hydroxyl radical believed to be the most damaging free radical in the body.

23) Açai has strong hydroxyl and peroxynitrite scavenging capacity based on the HORAC and NORAC antioxidant assays. Açai can reduce nitrosative stress due to the peroxynitrite radical.

24) A considerable amount of scientific literature supports a role for oxidative stress in the pathogenesis of age-related human diseases and a contribution of dietary polyphenols to their prevention.

25) Açai pulp has been shown that it can reduce oxidative stress due to naturally occurring processes such as oxygen metabolism and inflammatory processes.

26) An açai-based fruit juice, that does not clarify or filter freeze-dried or frozen açai, has been shown to increase levels of antioxidant activity in serum in healthy adults under oxidative stress, based on a randomized, double-blind, placebo-controlled, cross-over study in healthy adults.

27) An açai-based fruit juice, that does not clarify or filter freeze-dried or frozen açai, has been shown to increase levels of antioxidant compounds in serum in healthy adults under oxidative stress, based on a randomized, double-blind, placebo-controlled, cross-over study in healthy adults.

28) An açai-based fruit juice, that does not clarify or filter freeze-dried or frozen açai, consumed daily over a twelve week period has been shown to improve the range of motion and reduce pain of the lumbar spine and both knees in subjects participating in an open label clinical trial. Further research to substantiate these benefits and others experienced by subjects is warranted based on the statistically significant improvements reported.

29) The antioxidant compounds in açai can penetrate human cells and increase antioxidant protection.

30) The antioxidant compounds in açai have been shown to increase antioxidant activity in serum *in vivo* (in the body).

31) Açai has over 3,000 organic compounds known as phytochemicals, such as flavonoids, polyphenols, anthocyanins, and proanthocyanidins. A growing body of scientific literature numbering in the thousands is suggesting that the properties of many phytochemicals are associated with a range of potential health benefits.

32) The anthocyanins in açai have been found to be five times more potent than the same class of anthocyanins found in other antioxidant-rich berries touted for their health giving properties.

33) The two predominant anthocyanins in açai are cyanidin-3-glucoside and cyanidin-3-glucoside-coumaraterutinoside.

34) When abnormal cells are exposed to the flavonoid, cyanidin-3-rutinoside (C-3-R), they respond by releasing peroxides that selectively kill cancer cells. When healthy cells are exposed to C-3-R, they do not release peroxides. The predominant flavonoid in açai is C-3-R.

35) When rodents were exposed experimentally to a cancer-causing agent that results in esophageal tumors later in life, freeze-dried açai pulp inhibited their formation, number and reduced their size compared to control animals not given açai pulp.

36) Research on freeze-dried açai has found that it has potent anti-inflammatory activity *in vitro*.

37) Proteins in açai have considerable inhibitory activity towards human salivary alpha-amylase, a marker of stress in humans.

38) Açai is both a fast and slow antioxidant, based on the Total Anti-oxidant (TAO) assay.

39) Published research has shown that pre-treatment of human neutrophil cells (a type of white blood cell) with açai pulp resulted in significant reduction in reactive oxygen species (ROS) production, following exposure to hydrogen peroxide. The formation of ROS was significantly inhibited in neutrophils at a dilution of one part per trillion, suggesting it works at physiological levels.

40) Açai contains appreciable amounts of plant fats known as phytosterols. The predominant phytosterols in açai pulp are beta-sitosterol, campesterol, and sigmasterol. These compounds have been shown to have lipid-lowering properties.

41) Using a cyclooxygenase inhibitor assay, açai pulp has been found to have cyclooxygenase-2 (COX-2) inhibitory activity. One way to reduce acute or chronic inflammation is to inhibit the activity of COX-2.

42) Açai pulp contains all of the essential vitamins, minerals, and trace elements needed to support human health, with the exception of phylloquinone (vitamin K-1).

43) Açai pulp contains all of the essential amino acids, and many non-essential amino acids, involved in protein synthesis in the human body.

44) Açai is a good source of soluble and insoluble fiber. The insoluble fiber contains antioxidant polyphenols, hence should not be removed by clarification or filtration.

45) Açai pulp has less than 1/10th of a gram per 100 grams of sugar, hence is very low in sucrose content.

46) The sodium content of açai is very low, at just 0.25 percent.

47) Realization of the economic value of açai fruit in the Amazon has resulted in a decrease in harvesting the trees just for the heart-of-palm.

48) In 2007, the açai fruit became the top non-wood food product exported out of the eastern Amazon River delta region.

49) Harvesting of açai palm trees for their palm hearts declined significantly in 2007 due to the recognition of the value of the fruit.

50) Açai fruit and heart-of palm can be co-harvested using proper management of açai plantation (açaizais) without damaging biodiversity.

51) The Amazon is known as the "lungs of the Earth", providing 20% of the oxygen we breathe.

52) The açai palm contributes to the absorption of carbon in our atmosphere, as well as the production of oxygen.

Conclusion

Açai fruit has a long history of traditional use in South America. I look forward to seeing more research on this remarkable fruit from the Amazon. Only in this way can we eventually understand the full range of its nutritional and general health-enhancing benefits to humans.

What an amazing sequence of discoveries occurred over many years. Açai pulp has the highest Total ORAC and TEAC assay values of any food with the exception of some spices. Assays have also shown it exerts the highest superoxide scavenging activity of any food. Açai pulp has been experimentally shown to be able to quench superoxide, peroxynitrite, hydroxyl and peroxyl free radicals, using numerous antioxidant assays.

Açai pulp contain polyphenolics, powerful antioxidant compounds found in other fruits and berries known for their antioxidant capacities. In the laboratory, açai has been found to possess remarkable antioxidant activity in human cells, even when diluted down to one part per trillion.

Moreover, its nutritional composition shows a complete complement of vitamins, minerals, amino acids, and a high concentration of healthy unsaturated fatty acids, with little sugar, and lots of fiber. One has to wonder why it took so long to recognize the potential of this fruit as a source of nutrition outside of the Amazon, given how much of it there is and its history of use.

Maybe it is because we have lost touch with the rest of the developing world, and neglected the bounty of nutritious foods found in places like the Amazon. I am sure those natives in the Amazon would not be surprised by all this excitement over a palm fruit that grows right in their back yards. They have relied on it for hundreds of years as a daily part of their diet during the dry season.

One has to marvel at the profound innate knowledge that natives of the New World possessed for centuries, in selecting what to include in their diet. Given the many recently discovered nutritional and phytochemical attributes of açai, is it any wonder why Amazon residents consume this fruit with virtually every meal of the day? It would have been surprising to discover that they didn't do so based on what we have learned to date.

Açai is completely organic, needs no herbicides or fertilizers to grow, and can be cultivated or harvested in the wild. It produces fruit for most of the year is abundant, and stands as a guardian of the Amazon rain forest, providing a canopy of trees that protect all kinds of flora and fauna that live and thrive below it.

As news of the nutritional value and antioxidant benefit of açai reaches the attention of people throughout the Amazon, hopefully people will increasingly protect these palms from needless destruction. By doing so, they will protect the rain forest we call the "lungs of the Earth."

I personally hope that the preservation of these remarkable palm trees will help protect and perpetuate the remarkable ecosystem known as the Amazon rain forest. The Amazon has yet to reveal countless foods and botanical-based products with health giving properties. Already, large areas of Brazil have come under official protection. However, more reserves and national parks are needed in the eastern Amazon delta where the largest and thickest stands of açai palms are found. Without the willingness to protect this region the current rate of destruction could lead to half of the Amazon disappearing in our lifetime. If we lose too much more of the Amazon our planet will certainly suffer, for this is by far the largest rain forest in the world and its ability to absorb carbon and produce oxygen has no equal in the world. Its loss will be felt around the world by countless generations to come.

Although I was skeptical at first, the açai fruit does seem to possess characteristics of a "super food." But because there is no agreement as to how to define such a food, my belief remains that the best diet is still one that includes numerous fruits, berries, vegetables, and nuts, consumed daily. In a chapter I recently wrote for a text on bioactive foods, I shared with readers what the diets of indigenous natives of North America consumed before the arrival of Europeans. The evidence strongly supports the importance of plant foods in maintaining health.

I hope this book encourages more people around the world to visit the Amazon and experience the Amazon rain forest firsthand. Stand along side of an açai palm and marvel at its beauty and annual bounty. We are all guardians of this planet. Let's serve that role well.

Acknowledgements

To the many people in Brazil who are engaged in a never-ending battle to protect the rain forests and its treasures – thank you!

To the many scientists who contributed to our understanding of açai's composition and bioactivities, including: Xianli Wu, Gitte Jensen, Boxin Ou, Ronald Prior, Dejian Huang, Jim Kababick, John Owens, Amit Agarwal, Edward Shanbrom, David Bell, Tong Wu, Kelly Patterson, David Ager, Kathleen Benson, Marcie Mitzner, Kimberlee Redman, Charlene Mogle, Robert Beaman, and Janelle Barnes.

My appreciation to Kathryn Millhorn for finding so many elusive papers.

To Laura Schauss for her never ending support.

Special thanks goes to all the people who encouraged me to take time out of my busy schedule to update and revise this book.

Notes

In August 2009, Oprah Winfrey and her popular TV show's guest, Dr. Oz, a noted New York physician, had finally had enough. For two years companies were claiming that both celebrities endorsed sales of various açai and resveratrol supplements, as well as an assortment of vanity products. Without their approval, such endorsements were clear trademark infringements that had the potential of damaging their reputation. The reason many of these companies were using their names was to engage in credit card fraud or other schemes involving deceptive advertising.

When the first of these advertisements appeared on the Internet, one of my colleagues at work forwarded an example of an email that came into his email box with the subject heading: "Detoxify and Loss Weight With Açai Berry." As he had knowledge of the research we had been doing for years on açai, he asked: "Have you seen this. Is it true?" The answer is, no! Not only had we not found that açai had these properties, we knew of no research that could substantiate such a claim.

Unfortunately for those who rely on the Internet for personal or work reasons what began as a drizzle of emails opened like a flood gate of pop-up ads, advertising on social networking sites, and search engines claiming remarkable weight loss if you purchased their supplement products.

I started collecting these emails and recording the claims made in many of the pop-up ads, hoping that one of these might tell me where the research was performed and published that substantiated these wondrous claims. I also asked our library and information specialist to comb the world's literature any study that supported these claims. Result: zero. Not one study.

Then I received calls from companies we knew had products with açai in it. They asked: "Dr. Schauss, do you know of any studies to support these weight loss and detox claims?" I figured it was only a matter of time before government regulatory agencies stepped in to try and stop such false advertising. The first action came to my attention when a reporter for the *New York Times* who was investigating companies making these claims interviewed me. She reported to me that the Attorney General of Connecticut had taken action against several companies. The publication of that expose article in the Times was soon followed by a news release warning consumers about these companies and their claims that was released by the Center for Science in the Public Interest (CSPI), based in Washington, D.C. Prior to alerting its members and media, I received a call from the founder and Executive Director of CSPI, Dr. Michael Jacobsen, as he had known me since 1979 when he attended a seminar on nutrition and behavior I had taught in Chicago. As I would tell every reporter who called, I knew of no research to make such health claims.

When the law firms and entities representing Oprah Winfrey and Dr. Oz finally took legal action, I had a chance to examine the exhibits that were filed with the complaints. One company, ranked as the #1 offender and source of all these emails was based in Fort Lauderdale, Florida. The products they sold included several açai and resveratrol supplements. What shocked me was how many websites they had created linked to the same products. I counted 124 websites to sell 7 products. Some of the websites had names that suggested it came from television news programs, while others incorporated the name of Oprah Winfrey or Dr. Oz. The next company, based in Coral Gables, Florida, ranked #2 in the complaint sold four products and used 33 websites to market them on the Internet. The third ranked company was based in Des Moines, Iowa, with three products and 33 websites. The fourth ranked company had an address in San Diego, California, and had 28 websites. The fifth company was based in Las Vegas, Nevada. The sixth in Phoenix, Arizona, seventh in Huntington Station, New York, eighth was registered in Dover, Delaware, and so on, each accused of defrauding consumers.

As evidence piled up that many of these companies were failing to deliver products people had paid for, refused to refund money as promised, or never received product(s) ordered yet were being charged for them on their credit card, it suggested that some of these enterprises were organized and had resources warranting attention of the US Food and Drug Administration, the Internal Revenue Service, and the US Federal Trade Commission, as well as Attorney Generals in many states in which these operators conducted business.

Before the end of August 2009 the Attorney Generals in several states sent our press releases urging consumers "to be cautious of signing up for free trials of açai berry products." In the case of Illinois, the Attorney General filed lawsuits against three suppliers and their related entities, each of which were based in Florida who used a fulfillment center in Illinois, as well as another company based in Utah.

According to the State of Illinois' complaint, "the companies offer consumers a 'free trial' to entice them to sign up by providing a credit card number for shipping and handling charges. The companies us the 'free trial' period to hook the consumers into a continuity sales program, where consumers are often unaware that they have agreed to buy a monthly supply of açai berry supplements (or other health supplement products) for $29 or $39 per month unless they cancel their orders within 14 days. "The Attorney General revealed that, "Many consumers do not even receive shipment of the trial supplements before they are billed for the first monthly installment shipment. As part of this scam, consumers then find it very difficult to cancel future orders. The companies often bill consumers' credit cards for a few months supply before the consumers are able to cancel the orders or cancel their credit card payments."

Legal action has also been taken against a number of affiliate marketers. They use the Internet's search engines, web sites, pop-up ads, social networking sites, etc., to drive Internet traffic to suppliers' Web sites. For example, to keep up with any research that might be reported on açai, I would occasionally use one of several search engines to locate new publications on the subject. My use of the word, "açai", can result in my becoming a target, which explains why I would receive so many of these emails. It didn't matter to these affiliate marketers that they were engaging in false advertising and false endorsements, as they are generally paid by sellers for driving traffic to their sites. "The affiliates receive compensation when Internet users click-through to the sellers' sites and commission for sales resulting from traffic that they route to the sellers' site", according to the Attorney General of Illinois.

Rather than let them off the hook, claiming they were innocent parties just providing a service, they are being held accountable "for their role in a seedy marketing game that steers unsuspecting consumers to online schemes."

Will legal action "send a clear message to other marketers and networks in the business of designing misleading, traffic enticing schemes", according to the State of Illinois? Only time will tell.

The take home message is that consumers should be skeptical and educate themselves instead of believing endorsement claims particularly for weight loss products that sound too good to be true and lack scientific substantiation.

Before sending this book to press another scheme appeared, "Chinese açai", despite açai not being native to China or anywhere outside of South America.

References

Anderson AB. Os nomes e usos de palmeiras entre uma tribo de indios Yanomama. *Acta Amazonica*, 1977; 7: 5-13.

Anderson AB. Use and management of native forests dominated by açai palm (*Euterpe oleracea* Mart.) in the Amazon estuary. *Advances Economic Botany*, 1988; 6: 144-154.

Anderson AB and Jardim MAG. Costs and benefits of floodplain forest management by rural inhabitants in the Amazon estuary: A case study of açai palm production. In: Browder JO [ed.] *Fragile Lands of Latin America: Strategies for Sustainable Development*. Westview Press: Boulder, CO. 1989, pp. 114-129.

Araújo, CL, Bezerra IWL, Dantas IC, Lima TVS, Oliveira AS, Miranda MR, Leite EL, Sales MP. Biological activity of proteins from pulps of tropical fruits. *Food Chemistry*, 2004; 85: 107-110.

Arts IC and Hollman PC. Polyphenols and disease risk in epidemiological studies. *American Journal Clinical Nutrition*, 2005; 81(1 Suppl): 317S-325S.

Balee W. *Footprints of the Forest. Ka'apor Ethnobotany – The Historical Ecology of Plant Utilization by an Amazonian People*. Columbia University Press: New York, 1994.

Bank G and Schauss AG. Antioxidant testing: An ORAC update. *Nutraceuticals World*, 2004; 7: 68-71.

Bao Y, Fenwick R. [eds.] *Phytochemicals in Health and Disease*. Marcel Dekker: New York, 2004.

Beaglehole JC (Ed.). *The Endeavor Journal of Joseph Banks*, 1768-1771. Volume 1. Angus & Robertson: Wellington, 1962, pp. 200-201.

Bell DR, Moon HJ. Concentrations of extracts from Amazonian palm berry (*Euterpe oleracea* Martius) protect coronary arteries from damage following external exposure to superoxide. Poster presented at the Annual Meeting of the Federation of American Societies for Experimental Biology meeting, San Francisco, March 2009.

Berliner JA and Watson AD. A role for oxidized phospholipids in atherosclerosis. *New England Journal Medicine*, 2005; 9-11.

Blasa M, Gennari L, Angelino D, Ninfali P. Fruit and vegetable antioxidants in health. In: *Bioactive Foods in Promoting Health: Fruits and Vegetables*. Watson RR, Preedy V. [eds.] Taylor and Francis/Elsevier: Amsterdam, 2009, in press.

Borbalan AM, Zorro L, Guillen DA, Barroso CG. Study of the polyphenol content of red and white grape varieties by liquid chromatography-mass spectrometry and its relationship to antioxidant power. *Journal Chromatography*, 2003; 1012: 31-8.

Bors W, Michel C, Stettmaier K. In: *Flavonoids and Other Polyphenols (Methods in Enzymology Vol. 335)*; Packer, L. (Ed.) Academic Press: San Diego, 2001; p. 166-180.

Bradie N, Schauss AG. Soursop (*Annona muricata* L.) Composition, nutritional value, medicinal uses, and toxicology. In: *Bioactive Foods in Promoting Health:*

Fruits and Vegetables. Watson RR, Preedy V. [eds.] Taylor and Francis/Elsevier: Amsterdam, 2009, in press.

Brighenti F, Valtuena S, Pellegrini N, Ardigo D, Del Rio D, Salvatore S, Piatti P, Serafini M and Zavaroni I. *British Journal of Nutrition*, 2005; 93: 619-625.

Brondizio ES, Safar CAM, Siqueira AD. The urban market of açai fruit (*Euterpe oleracea* Mart.) and rural land use change: ethnographic insights into the role of price and land tenure constraining agricultural choices in the Amazon estuary. *Urban Ecosystems*, 2002; 6: 67-97.

Brondizio ES. *The Amazonian Caboclo and the Açai Palm: Forest Farmers in the Global Market.* New York Botanical Garden Press: New York, 2008.

Broschat TK, Meerow AW. *Ornamental Palm Horticulture.* University Press of Florida: Gainesville, 2000, pp. 61, 132.

Buettner GR. The pecking order of free radicals and antioxidants: lipid peroxidation, alpha-tocopherol, and ascorbate. *Arch Biochem Biophys*, 1993; 300:535-543.

Bushman BS, Phillips B, Isbell T, Ou B, Crane JM, Knapp SJ. Chemical composition of caneberry (Rubus spp.) seeds and oils and their antioxidant potential. *Journal Agricultural Food Chemistry*, 2004; 52: 7982-7987.

Bushway RJ, McGann DF, Cook WP, and Bushway AA. Mineral and vitamin content of lowbush blueberries (Vaccinium angustifolium Ait.). *Journal of Food Science*, 1983; 48: 1878-1879.

Cadenas E, Packer L. [eds.] *Handbook of Antioxidants. Second Edition.* Marcel Dekker: New York, 2002.

Cavalcante PB, Johnson D. Edible palm fruits of the Brazilian Amazon. In: Cavalcante: Edible Palm Fruits. *Frutas Comestiveis da Amazonia II.* Museu Goeldi: Belem, Brazil, 1974; and, Principes, 1977; 21: 91-102.

Chernela JM. *The Wanano Indians of the Brazilian Amazon: A Sense of Space.* University of Texas Press: Austin, TX, 1993, p. 112.

Chin Y-0W, Chai H-B, Keller WJ, Kinghorn AD. Lignans and other constituents of the fruits of *Euterpe oleracea* (açai) with antioxidant and cytoprotective activities. *Journal Agricultural Food Chemistry*, 2008; 56: 7759-7764.

Collins AR. Assays for oxidative stress and antioxidant status: Applications to research into the biological effectiveness of polyphenols. *American Journal Clinical Nutrition*, 2005; 81(Suppl.): 261S-267S.

De Brito ES, De Araujo MCP, Alves RE, Carkeet C, Clevidence BA, Novotny JA. Anthocyanins present in selected tropical fruits: acerola, jambolao, jussara, and guajiru. *Journal Agricultural Food Chemistry*, 2007; 55: 9389-9394.

Del Pozo-Insfran D, Percival SS, Talcott ST. Açai (*Euterpe oleracea* Mart.) polyphenolics in their glycoside and aglycones forms induce apoptosis of HL-60 leukemia cells. *Journal Agricultural Food Chemistry*, 2006; 54: 1222-1229.

Durak I, Avci A, Kacmaz M, Buyukkocak S, Cimen MY, Elgun S, Ozturk HS. Comparison of antioxidant potentials of red wine, white wine, grape juice and alcohol. *Current Medical Research Opinion*, 1999; 15:316-20.

Dyer AP. Latent energy in *Euterpe oleracea*. Universidad de Los Andes,

Escuela de Ingenieria Forestal, Laboratorio de Bioenergia, LABONAC, Merida, Venezuela. *Proceedings of the 9th Bioenergy Conference, Biomass Energy Environment*, 1996, pp. 733-738.

Editorial. The devil in the dark chocolate. *The Lancet*, 2007; 307: 2070.

Ellison D, and Ellison A. *Betrock's Cultivated Palms of the World.* Betrock Information Systems: Hollywood, FL, 2001, p. 110.

Edwards WH. V*oyage Up the River Amazon, Including a Residence at Para in 1846.* The Narrative Press: Santa Barbara, CA, 2004. (The original edition was published in New York by D. Appleton & Company in 1848.)

Erlejman AG, Verstraeten SV, Fraga CG, Oteiza, PI. The interaction of flavonoids with membranes: Potential determination of flavonoid antioxidant effects. *Free Radical Research*, 2004; 38: 1311-1320.

Ferreria AR. *Viagem Filosofica: Pelas Capitanias do Grao Para, Rio Negro, Mato Grosso e Cuiaba*, 1783-1792. Conselho Federal de Cultura: Rio de Janeiro, Brazil, 1971. (Drawing of Tanarana Indian gathering Açai fruit.)

Ferreira VLP, Graner M, Bovi MLA, Draetta IS, Paschoalino JE, and Shirose I. Compariç„o entre os palmitos das palmeiras *Guilielma gasipaes* Bailey (pupunha) *e Euterpe edulis* Mart. (juçara). I. Avaliaçıes fĺsicas, organolĒpticas e bioquìmicas. Colet,nea Inst. *Tecnologia de Alimentos*, Campinas. 1982; 12:255-272.

Ferreira VLP., Graner M, Bovi MLA, Figueiredo IB, Angelucci E, and Yokomizo Y. Compariç„o entre os palmitos das palmeiras Guilielma gasipaes Bailey (pupunha) *e Euterpe edulis* Mart. (juçara). II. Avaliaçıes fĺsicas e quìmicas. Colet,nea Inst. *Tecnologia de Alimentos*, Campinas. 1982; 12:273-282.

Finley JW. Phenolic antioxidants and prevention of chronic inflammation. *Food Technology*, 2004; 58: 42-46.

Food and Agriculture Organization of the United Nations. Food and fruit-bearing forest species. Examples from Latin America. Rome, Italy, 1986.

Gallori S, Bilia AR, Bergonzi MC, Barbosa WLR, and Vincieri FF. Polyphenolic constituents of fruit pulp of *Euterpe oleracea* Mart. (Açai palm). *Chromatographia*, 2004, 59: 739-743.

Granot E and Kohen R. Oxidative stress in childhood – in health and disease states. *Clinical Nutrition*, 2004; 23: 3-11.

Halvorsen BL, Carlsen MH, Phillips KM, Bohn SK, Holte K, Jacobs DR and Blomhoff R. Context of redox-active compounds (ie, antioxidants) in foods consumed in the United States. *Americal Journal Clinical Nutrition*, 2006; 84: 95-135.

Henderson A, Galeano G, Bernal R. *Field Guide to the Palms of the Americas.* Princeton University Press, Princeton, NJ, 1995, p. 123-124, 284-285.

Hodgson JM, Devine A, Burke V, Dick IM, Prince RL. Chocolate consumption and bone density in older women. *American Journal Clinical Nutrition*, 2008; 87: 175-180.

Honzel D, Carter SG, Redman KA, Schauss AG, Endres JR and Jensen GS. Comparison of chemical and cell-based antioxidant methods for evaluation of foods and natural products: Generating multifaceted data by parallel testing using erythrocytes and polymorphonuclear cells. *Journal Agriculture Food Chemistry*,

2008; 56: 8319–8325.

Huang, D, Ou B, Hampsch-Woodill M, Flanagan JA, Prior RL, Deemer EK. Development and validation of oxygen radical absorbance capacity assay for lipophilic antioxidants using randomly methylated beta-cyclodextrin as the solubility enhancer. *Journal Agricultural Food Chemistry*, 2002; 50: 1815-1821.

Huang D, Ou B, Hampsch-Woodill M, Flanagan JA, Prior RL. High-throughput assay of oxygen radical absorbance capacity (ORAC) using a multichannel liquid handling system coupled with a microplate fluorescence reader in 96-well format. *Journal Agricultural Food Chemistry*, 2002; 50: 4437-4444.

Huang D, Ou B, Prior RL. The chemistry behind antioxidant capacity assays. *Journal Agricultural Food Chemistry*, 2005; 53: 1841-1856.

Iaderoza M, Baldini VLS, Draetta I dos S, Bovi MLA. Anthocyanins from fruits of açai (*Euterpe oleracea*, Mart) and jucara (*Euterpe edulis*, Mart). *Tropical Sciences*, 1992; 32: 41-46.

INC magazine's 500/5000 ranking of Monavie in 2009 is reported at: http://inc.com/inc5000/2009/company-profile.html?id=200900180

Jardim MAG and Kageyama PY. Phenology of flowering and fruiting in a natural population of cabbage-palm (*Euterpe oleracea* Mart.) in the Amazon estuary. *Boletim do Museu Paraense Emilio Goeldi Serie Botanica*, 1994; 10: 77-82.

Jardim MA and Rombold JS. Effects of adubation and thinning on açai palm (*Euterpe oleracea* Mart.) fruit yield from a natural population. *Boletim do Museu Paraense Emilio Goeldi Serie Botanica*, 1994; 10: 283-293.

Jardim MAG. Aspectos da producao extrativista do Açaizeiro (*Euterpe oleracea* Mart.) no estuario Amazonico. *Boletim do Museu Paraense Emilio Goeldi Serie Botanica*, 1996; 12: 137-144.

Jardim MA and Rombold JS. Management of infloresecences Açai palm (*Euterpe oleracea* Mart.) in the Amazon river estuary. *Boletim do Museu Paraense Emilio Goeldi Serie Botanica*, 1998; 14: 53-62.

Jensen GS, Patterson KM, Barnes J, Carter SG, Wu, W, Scherwitz L, Beaman R, Endres JR, Schauss AG. *In vitro* and *in vivo* antioxidant and anti–inflammatory capacity of an antioxidant–rich fruit and berry juice blend. Results of a pilot and randomized, double–blind, placebo–controlled, crossover study. *Journal Agricultural Food Chemistry*, 2008: 56: 8326–8333.

Jensen GS, Schauss AG, Beaman R, Ager DM. Açai fruit (*Euterpe oleracea* Mart.): Systematic and collaborative study of the phytochemistry, nutrient composition, and *in vitro* and *in vivo* bioactivities of the Amazonian palm fruit in humans. *Alternative Therapies Health Medicine*, 2009; 15: S90-S91.

Jones DL. *Palms Throughout the World*. Smithsonian Institution Press: Washington, DC, 1995, p. 214.

Joseph JA, Nadeau DA, and Underwood, A. *The Color Code*. Hyperion: New York, 2002, pp. 18-19.

Joseph JA, Shukitt-Hale B, Casadesus G. Reversing the deleterious effects of aging on neuronal communication and behavior: Beneficial properties of fruit polyphenolic compounds. *American Journal Clinical Nutrition*, 2005; 81(Suppl.): 313S-316S.

Jordan M. In Brazil, a desperate struggle is waged over a salad garnish.

References

The Wall Street Journal, March 25, 2002, p. 1.

Kalokineros A. Every Second Child. Keats Publishing: New Canaan, CT, 1981.

Lambert JD, Hong J, Yang G, Liao J, Yang CS. Inhibition of carcinogenesis by polyphenols: Evidence from laboratory investigations. *American Journal of Clinical Nutrition*, 2005; 81: 285S-291S.

Lescure JP, Castro A-de. Extractivism in central Amazonia. *Bois et Forets des Tropiques*. 1992; 231: 35-51.

Li Y, Huang T-T, Carlson EJ, Melov S, Ursell PC, Olson JL, Noble LJ, Yoshimura MP, Berger C, Chan PH, Wallace DC, Epstein CJ. Dilated cardiomyopathy and neonatal lethality in mutant mice lacking manganese superoxide dismutase. *Nature Genetics*, 1995; 11: 376-381.

Liu RH. The potential health benefits of phytochemicals in berries for protecting against cancer and coronary heart disease. In: *Berry Fruit: Value-Added Products for Health Promotion*. Zhao Y [ed.]. CRC Press: Boca Raton, FL., pp. 187-203.

Matheus ME, Fernandes SB, Silveira CS, Rodriques VP, Menezes F, Fernandes PD. Inhibitory effects of *Euterpe oleracea* Mart. on nitric oxide production and iNOS expression. *Journal Ethnopharmacology*, 2006; 107: 291-296.

Meerow AW. *Betrock's Guide to Landscape Palms*. Betrock Information Systems: Cooper City, FL, 1992, p. 46.

Meerow AW. *Betrock's Guide to Landscape Palms*, Ninth Edition. Betrock Information Systems: Hollywood, FL, 2004, p. 46.

Mertens-Talcott SU, Rios J, Jilma-Stohlawetz P, Pacheco-Palencia LA, Meibohm B, Talcott ST, Derendorf H. Pharmacokinetics of anthocyanins and antioxidant effects after the consumption of anthocyanin-rich açai juice and pulp (*Euterpe olerace* Mart.) in human healthy volunteers. *Journal Agricultural Food Chemistry*, 2008; 56; 7796-7802.

Miranda-Rottman S, Aspillaga AA, Perez DD, Vasquez L, Martinez ALF and Leighton F. Juice and phenolic fractions of the berry Arstotelia chilensis inhibit LDL oxidation *in vitro* and protect human endothelial cells against oxidative stress. *Journal Agriculture Food Chemistry*, 2002; 50: 7542-7547.

Mora Urpí J and CR Clement. Races and populations of peach palm found in the Amazon basin, p. 79-94. In: C.R. Clement and L. Coradin (eds.). Final report (revised): Peach palm (*Bactris gasipaes*) germplasm bank. US-AID project report, Manaus, Brazil, 1988.

Mariani E, Polidori MC, Cherubini A, Mecocci P. Oxidative stress in brain aging, neurodegenerative and vascular diseases: An overview. *Journal Chromatography B*, 2005; 65-75.

McAnulty SR, McAnulty LS, Nieman DC, et al. Consumption of blueberry polyphenols reduces exercise-induced oxidative stress compared to Vitamin C. *Nutrition Research*, 2004; 24: 209-221.

Morell V. The rain forest in Rio's backyard. *National Geographic*, 2004; 205(4): 3-22.

Muller FL, Song W, Liu Y, Chaudhuri A, Pieke-Dahl, Strong R, Huang T-T, Epstein CJ, Roberts LJ, Csete M, Faulkner JA, Van Remmen H. Absence of CuZn superoxide dismutase leads to elevated oxidative stress and acceleration of age-dependent skeletal muscle atrophy. *Free Radical Biology Medicine*, 2006; 40: 1993-2004.

Muniz-Miret N, Vamos R, Hiraoka M, Montagnini F, Mendelsohn RO. The economic value of managing the Açai plant (*Euterpe oleracea* Mar.) of the floodplains of the Amazon estuary, Para, Brazil. *Forest Ecology Management*, 1996; 87: 163-173.

Neto MAM, Alves JD, Oliveira de- EM. Anaerobic metabolism of *Euterpe oleracea*. II. Plant tolerance mechanism to anoxia. *R Bras Fisiol Veg*, 1995; 7: 47-51.

Niculescu L, Stancu, C, Sima A, Toporan D, Simionescu M. The total peroxyl radical trapping potential in serum – an assay to define the stage of atherosclerosis. *Journal Cellular Molecular Medicine*. 2007; 5: 285-294.

Okonogi S, Duangrat C, Anuchpreeda S, Tachakittirungrod S, Chowwanapoonpohn S. Comparison of antioxidant capacities and cytotoxicities of certain fruit peels. *Food Chemistry*, 2007; 103: 839-846.

Orhan H, Van Holland B, Krab B, Moeken J, Vermeulen NPE, Hollander P, Meerman, JHN. Evaluation of a multi-parameter biomarker set for oxidative damage in man: Increased urinary excretion of lipid protein and DNA oxidation products after one hour of exercise. *Free Radical Research*, 2004; 38: 1269-1279.

Ou B, Hampsch-Woodill M, Prior RL. Development and validation of an improved oxygen radical absorbance capacity assay using fluorescein as the fluorescent probe. *Journal Agricultural Food Chemistry*, 2001; 49: 4619-4626.

Ou B, Huang D, Hampsch-Woodill M, Flanagan JA, Deemer EK. Analysis of antioxidant activities of common vegetables employing oxygen radical absorbance capacity (ORAC) and ferric reducing antioxidant power (FRAP) assays: a comparative study. *Journal Agricultural Food Chemistry*, 2002; 50: 3122-3128.

Ou B, Hampsch-Woodill M, Flanagan J, Deemer EK, Prior RL, Huang D. Novel fluorometric assay for hydroxyl radical prevention capacity using fluorescein as the probe. *Journal Agricultural Food Chemistry*, 2002; 50: 2772-2777.

Ou B, Huang D, Hampsch-Woodill M, Flanagan JA. When east meets west: the relationship between yin-yang and antioxidant-oxidation. *FASEB J*, 2003; 17: 127-129.

Pan M-H, Lai C-S, Dushenkov S, Ho C-T. Modulation of inflammatory genes by natural dietary bioactive compounds. *Journal Agricultural Food Chemistry*, 2009; 57: 4467-4477.

Pannala AS and Rice-Evans C. In: *Flavonoids and Other Polyphenols (Methods in Enzymology Vol. 335)*; Packer, L. Ed. Academic Press: San Diego, 2001; pp. 266-72.

Paula de- JE. Anatomia de *Euterpe oleracea* Mart. (Palma da Amazonia). *Acta Amazonia*, 1975; 5: 265-278.

Perricone N. The Perricone Promise: *Look Younger, Live Longer in Three Easy Steps*. Warner Books: New York, 2004.

Perricone, N. *The Perricone Weight-loss Diet*. Ballantine Books: New York, 2005.

Peters CM, Balick MJ, Kahn F, Anderson AB. Oligarchic forests of economic plants in Ammonia: Utilization and conservation of an important tropical resource.

Conservation Biology, 1989; 3: 341-349.

Plotkin MJ, Balick MJ. Medicinal uses of South American palms. *Journal Ethnopharmacology*, 1984; 10: 157-179.

Pollack H, Mattos M, Uhl C. A profile of palm heart extraction in the Amazon estuary. *Human Ecology*, 1995; 23: 357-385.

Pollan M. The Omnivore's Dilemma: *A Natural History of Four Meals.* Penguin Group: New York, 2006.

Pollan M. *In Defense of Food.* Penguin Press: New York, 2008.

Pozo-Insfran D, Brenes CH, Talcott ST. Phytochemical composition and pigment stability of açai (*Euterpe oleracea* Mart.). *Journal Agricultural Food Chemistry*, 2004; 52: 1539-1545.

Prior RL, Hoang H, Gu L, Wu X, Bacchiocca M, Howard L, Hampsch-Woodill M, Huang D, Ou B, Jacob R. Assays for hydrophilic and lipophilic antioxidant capacity (oxygen radical absorbance capacity (ORACFL)) of plasma and other biological and food samples. *Journal Agricultural Food Chemistry*, 2003; 51: 3273-3279.

Prior RL, Wu X, Schaich K. Standardized methods for the determination of antioxidant capacity and phenolics in foods and dietary supplements. *Journal Agriculture and Food Chemistry*, 2005; 53: 4290-4302.

Queiroz JA, Mochiutti S, Machado SA, Galvao F. Floristic composition and forest's structure in Amazon estuarine high floodplain. *Floresta*, 2005; 35: 41-56.

Qin Y, Xia M, Ma J, Hao Y, Liu J, Mou H, Cao L, Ling W. Anthocyanin supplementation improves serum LDL- and HDL-cholesterol concentrations associated with the inhibition of cholesteryl ester transfer protein in dyslipidemic subjects. *American Journal Clinical Nutrition*, 2009; 90: 485-492.

Rodriques de Areia ML, Miranda MA, Hartmann T. *Memory of Amazonia: Alexandre Rodriues Ferreira and the Viagem Philosphica in the Captaincies of Grao-Para, Rio Negro, Mato Grosso, and Cuyaba.* Museum of the Department of Anthropology, University of Coimbra, Portugal, 2003, plate 27.

Rodriques KF. The foliar fungal endophytes of the Amazonian palm *Euterpe oleracea. Mycololgia*, 1994; 86: 376-385.

Schauss, AG, Wu X, Prior RL, Ou B, Huang D, Owens J, Agarwal A, Jensen GS, Hart AN, Shanbrom E. Antioxidant capacity and other bioactivities of the freeze-dried Amazonian palm berry, *Euterpe oleracea*e Mart. (açai). *Journal Agricultural Food Chemistry*, 2006a, 54(22): 8604-8610.

Schauss, AG, Wu X, Prior RL, Ou B, Patel D, Huang D, Kababick JP. Phytochemical and nutrient composition of the freeze-dried Amazonian palm berry, *Euterpe oleracea*e Mart. (açai). *Journal Agricultural Food Chemistry*, 2006b, 54(22): 8598-8603.

Schauss AG, Wu X, Ou B, Jensen GS, Agarwal A. High radical oxygen scavenging and antioxidant activity in freeze-dried *Euterpe oleracea* palm fruit pulp. *Federation Societies Experimental Biology Journal*, 2006; 20(4): A145.

Schauss AG. Obesity: *Why Are Men Getting Pregnant (Intra-abdominal Adiposity).* Basic Health: Los Angeles, 2006.

Schauss AG. Extraordinary antioxidant activity and nutritional content of a small palm fruit *Euterpe oleracea* ("açai") from the Amazon. Oral presentation at the 236th American Chemical Society National Meeting, Division of Agricultural and Food Chemistry Symposium on Flavor and Health Effects of Small Fruits. Philadelphia, PA, August 18, 2008. [Abstract] *Cornucopia*, Fall, 2008, AGFD 95.

Schauss AG. Emerging knowledge of the bioactivity of foods in the diets of indigenous North Americans. In: *Bioactive Foods in Promoting Health: Fruits and Vegetables*. Watson RR, Preedy V. [eds.] Taylor and Francis/Elsevier: Amsterdam, 2009, in press.

Schauss AG, Jensen GS, Wu X. Increased antioxidant capacity and inhibition of lipid peroxidation in healthy adults consuming Monavie Active, an açai (*Euterpe oleracea*) fruit based juice. *Acta Horticulturae*, 2009, in press.

Schauss AG. Açai (*Euterpe oleracea* Mart.): A macro and nutrient rich palm fruit from the Amazon rain forest with demonstrated bioactivities *in vitro* and *in vivo*. In: *Bioactive Foods in Promoting Health: Fruits and Vegetables*. Watson RR, Preedy V [eds.]. Taylor and Francis/Elsevier: Amsterdam. 2009, *in press*.

Serafini M, Maiani G, and Ferro-Luzzi A. Free red wine enhances plasma antioxidant activity in humans. *Journal of Nutrition*, 1998 128: 1003-7.

Serafini M, Maiani G, and Ferro-Luzzi A. Inhition of human LDL lipid peroxidation by phenol-rich beverages and their impact on plasma total antioxidant capacity in humans. *Journal of Nutrition*, 2000 11: 585-90.

Shimkokomaki M, Abdala C, et al. Anatomy of *Euterpe oleracea* Mart. (Palmae of the Amazonia). Acta Amazonica, 1975; 5: 265-278.

Sick H. *Birds in Brazil: A Natural History*. Princeton University Press: Princeton, NJ, 1993, pp. 45, 447.

Siriwoharn T, Wrolstad RE, Finn CE, Pereira CB. Influence of cultivar, maturity, and sampling on blackberry (Rubus L. hydrids) anthocyanins, polyphenolics, and antioxidant properties. *Journal Agriculture Food Chemistry*, 2004; 52: 8021-8030.

Skaper SD, et al. *Free Radical Biology and Medicine*, 1997 22: 669-78.

Stevenson GB. *Palms of South Florida*. University Press of Florida: Gainesville, FL, 1996, p. 220.

Strudwick J, Sobel GL. Uses of *Euterpe oleracea* Mart. in the Amazon estuary, Brazil. In: *The Palm – Tree of Life: Biology, Utilization and Conservation*. Balick MJ [ed.] Advances in Economic Botany, Volume 6. New York Botanical Garden: Bronx, NY, 1988, pp. 225-253.

Sumner J. *The Natural History of Medicinal Plants*. Timber Press: Portland, OR, 2000.

Surh Y-J, Dong Z, Cadenas E, Packer L. *Dietary Modification of Cell Signaling Pathways*. CRC Press: Boca Raton, FL, 2009.

The Emerald Realm: Earth's Precious Rain Forests. National Geographic Society: Washington, DC, 1990.

Wiley RA. BioBalance: *The Acid/Alkaline Solution to the Food-Mood-Health Puzzle*. Life Sciences Press: Tacoma, 1989.

Zou S, Carey JR, Liedo P, Ingram DK, Müller, HG, Wang J-L, Yao F, Yu B, Zhou A. The prolongevity effect of resveratrol depends on dietary composition and calorie intake in a tephritid fruit fly. *Experimental Gerontology*, 2009; 44: 472-476.

Index

Index

Index